Helen Kavanagh

Shortcuts to Success

GEOGRAP...

Leaving Certificate
Sample Answers
Physical and Regional

Specimen Copy
With the compliments of
Frances Kelly
Contact no: 086 2437751
Email: fkelly@gillmacmillan.ie   www.gillmacmillan.ie

GILL & MACMILLAN

Gill & Macmillan Ltd
Hume Avenue
Park West
Dublin 12
with associated companies throughout the world
www.gillmacmillan.ie

© Dan Sheedy, 2009
Artwork by Replika Press Pvt Ltd, India

978 0 7171 4553 9

Print origination by Replika Press Pvt Ltd, India

*The paper used in this book is made from the wood pulp of managed
forests. For every tree felled, at least one tree is planted, thereby renewing
natural resources.*

Contents

Section **1**
Physical Geography

Questions on physical geography in the Leaving Certificate consist of shorter questions worth eight marks each, and longer questions worth twenty or thirty marks each. To facilitate this, each topic in this section is divided into two parts. The first part deals with the information required to answer short questions and the second part provides sample answers to frequently asked long questions. The long questions appear in the text with an 'LQ' before them.

The topics covered in this section are:

Topic **1**
The Internal Structure of the Earth

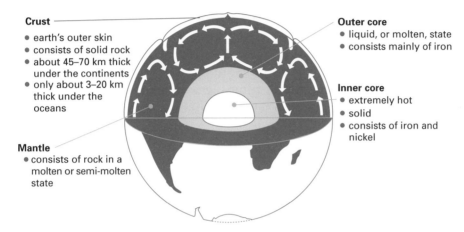

Crust
- earth's outer skin
- consists of solid rock
- about 45–70 km thick under the continents
- only about 3–20 km thick under the oceans

Mantle
- consists of rock in a molten or semi-molten state

Outer core
- liquid, or molten, state
- consists mainly of iron

Inner core
- extremely hot
- solid
- consists of iron and nickel

Figure 1 The internal structure of the earth

Core
- The earth's **inner core** is solid and consists of iron and nickel.
- The earth's **outer core** is liquid and consists of iron.

Mantle
The earth's mantle consists of molten/melting rock called **magma**. When magma reaches the surface it is called **lava**.

- The earth's **lower mantle** consists of liquid magma.
- The earth's **upper mantle** consists of almost solid rock.

Crust
The earth's crust is the solid rock that is found beneath the land and the sea.

- **Continental crust** is thick (60 km), and composed of light rocks made from silica and alumina (SIAL).
- **Oceanic crust** is thinner (10 km), and composed of heavy rocks made from silica and magnesium (SIMA).

Lithosphere
Lithosphere is the term given to the earth's crust and the solid upper mantle.

Asthenosphere
Asthenosphere is the name given to the line between the liquid lower mantle and the solid upper mantle.

Plate tectonics

The theory of plate tectonics was first proposed by Alfred Wegener. He proposed that the earth's crust is divided into sections called **plates**. These plates float on the earth's mantle and move as a result of convection currents.

Convection currents
Plates move due to convection currents. Magma near the core is heated intensely. As magma is heated it becomes less dense than the surrounding magma and begins to rise. As it rises it moves away from the core and begins to cool. As the magma cools it becomes more dense, which causes it to flow sideways dragging the overlying plate with it.

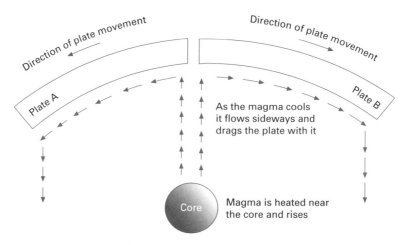

Figure 2 Convection currents

Continental drift
The theory of continental drift supports the theory of plate tectonics. It suggests that the continents which exist today were once part of a super-continent called Pangaea. Pangaea broke up between 200 and 300 million years ago and the resulting continents gradually drifted apart, due to convection currents, until they reached their current location.

Proof of plate tectonics
- **Continental fit**: the continents of the world seem to fit together like a jigsaw, which suggests they were once part of the same continent.

- **Fossils and geology**: similar rock types and fossils have been found on different continents, for example South America and Africa, even though they are separated by thousands of kilometres of ocean.
- **Marine sediments**: marine fossils have been found in the Himalayas, supporting the theory of plate movement and collision.

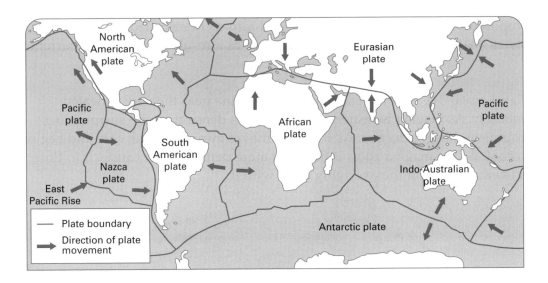

Figure 3 Plates of the earth's crust

Plate margins in North America

The North American plate contains an active plate margin and a trailing plate margin.

The **active plate margin** is found on the west coast of North America. This is called an active plate margin as it is the part of the plate which is moving alongside another plate (the Pacific plate). This is now a neutral plate boundary, with the two plates sliding past each other. In the past, however, it was a destructive plate boundary that led to the formation of mountain ranges such as the Rocky Mountains. As a result most rocks found in the region are **igneous rocks**.

The **trailing plate margin** is found on the east coast. This area represents the middle of the plate and therefore does not experience any seismic or volcanic activity. Sediments which were eroded from the mountains in the west were deposited here, which led to the formation of **sedimentary rocks** in this region.

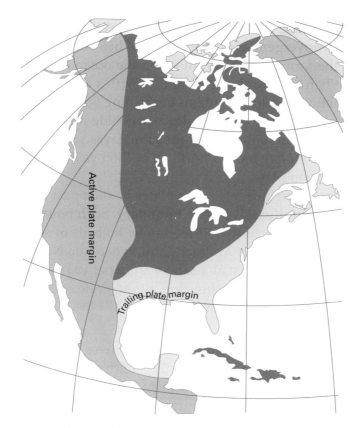

Figure 4 North America's plate margins

1. Explain the process of global crustal plate movement as it is currently understood.

The process of global crustal plate movement is based on the theory that plates move by means of convection currents. Magma near the core is heated intensely. As magma is heated it becomes less dense than the surrounding magma which allows it to rise. As it rises however it moves away from the core and begins to cool and become denser. This causes the magma to flow sideways and as it does so it drags the overlying plate with it. Because the plates move like this they can separate, collide or slide past each other.

When plates separate it creates a **constructive/divergent plate boundary**. This commonly occurs when two oceanic plates separate. As the plates separate a trench forms on the ocean floor. Magma from the mantle moves upwards to fill this trench. When the magma reaches the surface (as lava) it cools rapidly forming large ridges of granite or basalt. Such features are called mid-oceanic ridges and an example is the Mid-Atlantic Ridge.

When convection currents cause plates to collide it is referred to as a **destructive/convergent plate boundary**. When two oceanic plates collide it leads to the formation of volcanoes on the ocean floor, e.g. the islands of Japan. When an oceanic plate collides with a continental plate it leads to the formation of fold mountains containing volcanoes, e.g. the Rocky Mountains. When two continental plates collide it also leads to the formation of fold mountains, e.g. the Himalayas which were formed when the Indian plate moved north 60 million years ago and collided with the Eurasian plate.

When convection currents cause plates to slide past each other it is known as a **neutral/passive plate boundary**. Such boundaries are usually free of any volcanic activity but tend to be hotbeds of seismic activity. An example of this is the San Andreas Fault, where the North American plate is moving north-west at a rate of 1 cm per year while the Pacific plate is moving in the same direction but at a rate of 6 cm per year.

LQ 2. Discuss the extent to which Ireland's location has changed over time.

Ireland's location has changed dramatically over the past 800 million years. It has moved from a position 30° south of the equator 400 million years ago to its present location at 53°N. This is due to the movement of plates as a result of convection currents in the mantle. This movement is responsible for all of Ireland's mountain ranges, rock types and landscape features. It is estimated that Ireland's movement covered a distance of almost 10,000 km over a period of over 800 million years.

Eight hundred million years ago, the present-day island of Ireland was two separate landmasses. The southern half of the country lay close to the South Pole while the northern half lay roughly 60° south of the equator. The southern part gradually moved northwards and, around 400 million years ago, collided with the northern part, which was at the time part of the American plate.

This collision is known as the Caledonian fold movement and led to Ireland becoming a single landmass for the first time. The mountain ranges that formed in Ireland in this period include the Nephin Beg Mountains and the Maumturk Mountains. This period also saw the development of the Leinster batholith, which formed when large amounts of magma seeped into the crust beneath Leinster.

Ireland then continued to drift north and 380 million years ago had almost reached the equator. At this point only the northern portion of the country remained above sea level. Large rivers were eroding the newly formed mountains significantly and this sediment was deposited in the sea, which covered the south. This sediment compacted on the sea floor (now Counties Cork and Kerry) to form old red sandstone.

About 350 million years ago there was a major rise in sea levels. At this point most of Ireland lay beneath a warm tropical ocean. The remains of sea creatures accumulating on the sea floor led to the formation of Carboniferous limestone in this period. Ireland continued to drift north.

When the African plate moved north and collided with the Eurasian plate 250 million years ago, this collision led to the formation of Macgillycuddy's Reeks and the Munster ridge and valley province. At this point Ireland lay across the Tropic of Cancer, near the location of the present-day Sahara.

Two hundred million years ago the mountain ranges of Ireland continued to be eroded and this led to the formation of new red sandstone.

By about 100 million years ago Ireland had reached 35°N and in this period Ireland's chalk formed.

Finally, about 65 million years ago there was a burst of volcanic activity and Ireland was separated from the American plate, which led to the beginnings of the Atlantic Ocean. The Antrim–Derry plateau also formed in this period.

Topic **2**
Volcanic Activity

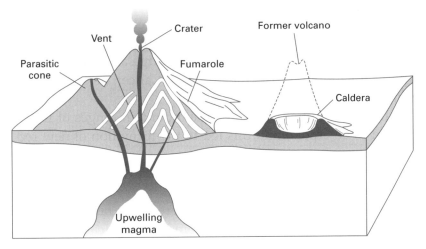

Figure 5 The internal structure and features of a volcano

Magma chamber
A magma chamber is that part of the earth's crust which the magma melts as it moves towards the surface.

Vent
A vent is the chimney-like funnel which the magma moves through in order to reach the surface.

Crater
A crater is the point where material is emitted into the atmosphere during an eruption.

Fumarole
A fumarole is a smaller crater where steam and gas are emitted into the atmosphere.

Layers
The layers of a volcano represent the material that was deposited after each eruption.

Parasitic cone
A parasitic cone is a smaller, secondary cone attached to the main cone.

Caldera
A caldera is a depression in the landscape which remains when the volcanic cone is blown away by a super-eruption or broken down by weathering and erosion.

Materials emitted by a volcano during an eruption

- **Lava** is molten rock that has reached the surface.

	Basic lava	Acidic lava
Silica content	Low	High
Temperature	1,000°C	800°C
Viscosity	Low	High
Speed	Travels quickly	Travels slowly

- **Volcanic gases:** carbon monoxide, carbon dioxide, sulphur and hydrogen.
- **Pyroclastic materials** are the large amounts of rock which are emitted during an eruption in the form of ash, cinders and bombs.
- **Pumice** are rocks with so many air spaces that they are light enough to float on water.

Types of volcanic cone

- **Cinder cones** are formed by violent eruptions where volcanic particles produce a steep-sided cone with a more gentle base.
- **Composite cones** are large, almost symmetrical volcanoes made of alternate layers of lava and pyroclastic material.
- **Dome cones** are formed of viscous, acidic lava where the lava is so thick that it can only travel a short distance.
- **Shield cones** occur when successive flows of basic lava with a low viscosity travel a long distance before cooling to form solid rock.

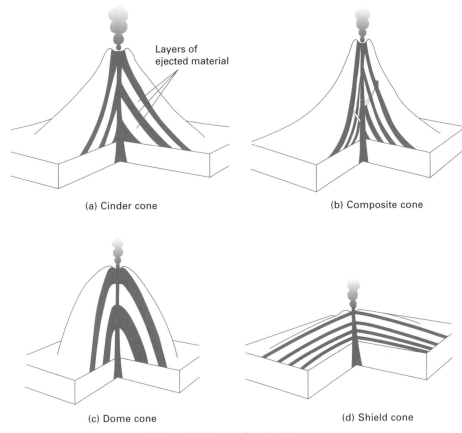

(a) Cinder cone

(b) Composite cone

(c) Dome cone

(d) Shield cone

Figure 6 Types of volcanic cone

Predicting volcanic eruptions

The main ways of predicting volcanic activity include:

- Using **seismographs** to record the tiny earthquakes that occur as magma rises
- Using **tiltmeters** to detect any swelling in the cone
- Monitoring levels of **sulphur dioxide** which tend to increase before an eruption.

Effects of volcanic activity

- Geothermal energy
- Geysers
- Fertile soils
- Tourism
- Loss of life

LQ 1. Discuss how plate tectonics has influenced the global distribution of volcanoes.

The first way in which plate tectonics has influenced the global distribution of volcanoes can be seen by the presence of volcanoes at **destructive plate boundaries**. Volcanoes at destructive boundaries are among the most violent forms of natural activity in the world. Such volcanoes can occur when an oceanic plate collides with another oceanic plate or with a continental plate.

When two plates collide, the heavier plate subducts beneath the lighter plate. As the subducting plate descends into the mantle it begins to melt at a depth of roughly 80 km. The melting plate releases very hot plumes of magma towards the surface. Because this magma came from a melting plate it contains large amounts of silica. This magma may simply melt into the overlying crust where it cools to form rock or it may force its way to the surface to form volcanoes.

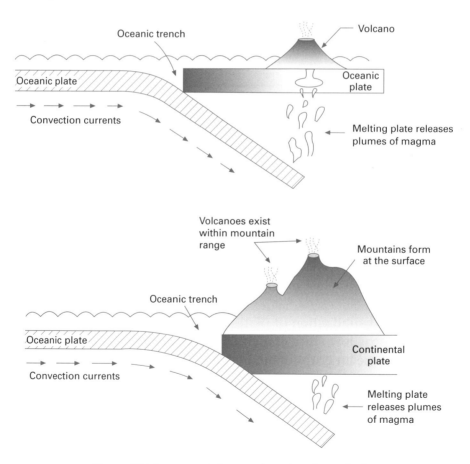

Figure 7 Volcanoes at destructive plate boundaries

Volcanoes at destructive boundaries are violent due to the magma's high silica content. The silica gas expands as the magma approaches the surface and the resulting build-up of pressure leads to a violent eruption. The islands of Japan are an example of volcanic activity at a destructive plate boundary.

The second way in which plate tectonics has influenced the global distribution of volcanoes can be seen by the presence of volcanoes at **constructive plate boundaries**. Volcanoes at constructive plate boundaries tend to be less dangerous than those which occur at destructive boundaries. Such volcanoes usually occur when two oceanic plates separate.

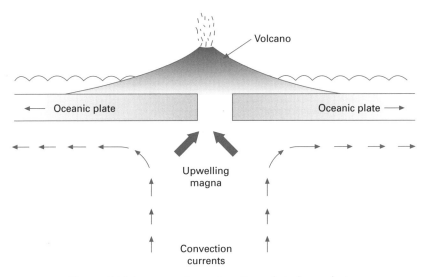

Figure 8 Volcanoes at constructive plate boundaries

As oceanic plates separate, magma from the mantle moves upwards to attempt to fill the trench in the ocean floor which has been created by the diverging plates. When magma reaches the surface it is referred to as lava.

Because no subduction of plates is involved, magma at constructive boundaries has low silica content. This means that there is no build-up of pressure before an eruption and eruptions are relatively non-violent. As the lava emitted is basic lava it tends to travel long distances. Volcanoes at these boundaries tend to have shield cones. The Mid-Atlantic Ridge is an example of volcanic activity at a constructive plate boundary.

The above answer is sufficient for this particular question, however other questions may require you to demonstrate your understanding of hot spots.

Volcanoes at hot spots

Although most volcanic activity takes place at plate boundaries, numerous volcanoes have formed away from plate boundaries. It is believed that hot spots are the reason for this.

A hot spot is an unusually hot area of magma beneath the earth's surface. A hot spot forces plumes of magma towards the surface and up against the overlying plate. Although the hot spot remains in the same place, the overlying plate will move across it. As the plate moves, the plumes of magma move upwards through fractures in the plate and can lead to the formation of a volcano.

Eventually the plate will move on and the magma will move upwards through a new fracture, forming a new volcano. In this way a string of islands can form in the middle of a plate. This is known as a mid-plate, volcanic island arc, for example the Hawaiian Islands.

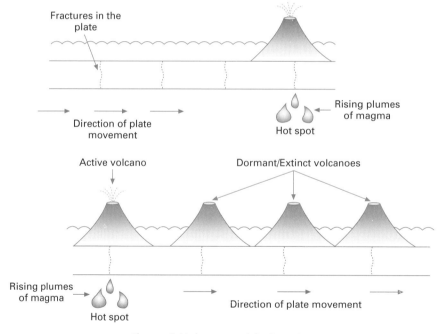

Figure 9 Volcanoes at hot spots

LQ **2. Discuss the formation of any two intrusive features formed within the earth's crust.**

Intrusive features/rocks occur when magma from the mantle forces its way up into the earth's crust but does not reach the surface. Instead it melts the rock in the crust and then cools to form an intrusive rock, such as granite, inside the crust. Intrusive rocks are also called plutonic rocks.

The first intrusive features I have studied are **sills** and **dykes**. A dyke is produced when a vertical plume of magma is injected up into the crust through a fracture in the crust. The pressure of the magma widens the fracture. Eventually the magma will cool to form a vertical sheet of granite called a dyke. Sills occur when magma is injected horizontally between layers of sedimentary rock close to the surface. Again the magma will melt the surrounding rock before cooling to form a horizontal layer of granite called a sill. If the magma pushes the overlying rock upwards a laccolith sill forms. If the magma pushes the underlying rock downwards a loppolith sill is formed. Examples of sills and dykes can be found beneath the crust of the Antrim–Derry plateau.

The second intrusive feature that I have studied is a **batholith**. Batholiths are also intrusive/plutonic features which are formed when magma from the mantle is forced into the crust where it cools and solidifies to form granite. Batholiths occur on a much larger scale than sills and can be over 30 km deep and hundreds of kilometres wide. Unlike sills, batholiths do not occur when magma seeps into the crust through fractures but instead occur when large amounts of magma move up into the crust and melt the crust which lies there.

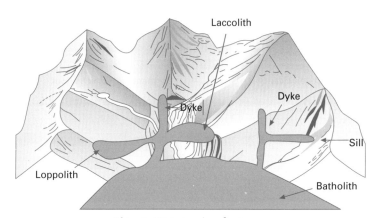

Figure 10 Intrusive features

Batholiths can become the surface when the overlying layers of rocks are removed by denudation (weathering and erosion). They can also be exposed to the surface when plates collide and buckle the crust forming fold mountains.

The Leinster batholith runs for 120 km from Dublin to Kilkenny and was brought to the surface 400 million years ago during the Caledonian fold movement, which formed the Dublin and Wicklow Mountains. The Caledonian fold movement is the name given to the collision of the Eurasian plate and the American plate.

LQ 3. Discuss the formation of any two extrusive (surface) features formed by volcanic activity.

Extrusive features form when magma seeps through the overlying crust and reaches the surface as lava. The first extrusive feature I have studied is a **volcano at a destructive boundary**. Volcanoes at destructive boundaries are the most violent form of volcanic activity. Such volcanoes can occur when two oceanic plates collide or when a continental plate collides with an oceanic plate.

When two plates collide, the heavier plate subducts beneath the lighter plate. As the subducting plate descends into the mantle it will begin to melt at a depth of roughly 80 km. This melting plate releases very hot plumes of magma towards the surface. Because this magma came from a melting plate it contains large amounts of silica. This magma may simply melt into the overlying crust where it cools to form rock or it may force its way to the surface to form volcanoes. Volcanoes at destructive boundaries are violent due to their high silica content. The silica gas expands as the magma approaches the surface and the resulting build-up of pressure leads to a violent eruption. The islands of Japan are an example of volcanic activity at a destructive plate boundary.

The second extrusive feature I have studied is a **basalt plateau**. A basalt plateau is an extrusive/volcanic feature formed when magma from the mantle is pushed up through large cracks in the crust. The lava flows quietly over the surface and usually spreads evenly across the landscape. When it cools it forms an igneous rock called basalt, and usually leaves a very flat relief, i.e. a plateau. Because the lava found at such locations is generally basic lava, it can flow for very large distances, e.g. the Antrim–Derry plateau.

Many basalt plateaux have a stepped appearance. This occurs because later lava flows did not travel as far as previous ones. The Giant's

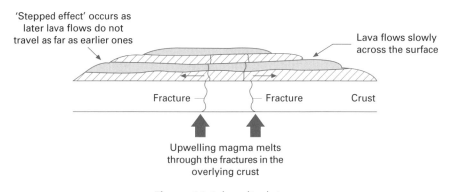

Figure 11 A basalt plateau

Causeway in Co. Antrim was formed in a similar manner when lava cooled slowly and contracted in a river valley to produce almost 60,000 hexagonal columns.

LQ

4. **Discuss two ways in which humans have benefited from volcanic activity.**

Or

Examine one positive and one negative effect of volcanic activity.

> *Choose two of the following three areas to answer the particular question asked in the exam.*

The first positive effect of volcanic activity I have studied is **geothermal energy.** The popularity and frequency of use of this environmentally friendly form of energy has increased greatly in recent years.

Geothermal energy harnesses the energy produced by plumes of magma as they rise into the earth's crust. Magma most commonly seeps into the overlying crust at plate margins or at hot spots and it is at these locations where the power is harnessed. As magma rises into the overlying rocks it melts some rocks completely but only heats other parts of the crust. The rocks which have been heated in turn heat the large amounts of water which have accumulated above them.

The heat generated by the magma is so great that it is capable of heating the water to almost 1,000°C. This is referred to as super-heating of water. The water does not evaporate because of the pressure being exerted on it by overlying rocks. The potential energy of this super-heated water can then be harnessed by humans by piping down cold water to this hot water. In this way both steam and hot water are forced to the surface where they are connected to turbines which in turn generate geothermal power.

Iceland's location on the Mid-Atlantic Ridge helps supply it with large amounts of geothermal energy. This energy is used in the central heating systems of homes, offices and industry.

A second positive effect of volcanic activity in modern society is that volcanic features are attractive **tourist destinations**. Volcanoes such as Mount Vesuvius and Mount Etna in Italy attract millions of tourists each year. The cities of Pompeii and Herculaneum, which were destroyed by a super-eruption of Vesuvius in 79 AD, are among Italy's premier tourist attractions.

Less violent forms of volcanic activity such as geysers and hot springs also attract tourists. In the USA, Hot Springs National Park in Arkansas attracts over one hundred thousand visitors per year, and the 'Old faithful' geyser in Yellowstone National Park, Wyoming, which erupts each hour, is another major draw for tourists.

The development of a thriving tourist sector around volcanoes has many benefits for the local population apart from the obvious revenue generated. Improvements in infrastructure designed to cater for increasing tourist numbers also improve the quality of life for locals. Also, because tourism is labour intensive, it generates large-scale employment in the tertiary sector which benefits the unskilled population.

Although volcanic activity can have many benefits for humans in the long term, in the short term it can have devastating effects, causing **loss of life** on a large scale. The most obvious damage produced by volcanic activity occurs during an eruption or super-eruption of an active volcano. For example the super-eruption of Mount Vesuvius in 79 AD killed over 20,000 people.

During an eruption many materials are emitted into the atmosphere which can cause damage to humans. Volcanoes emit toxic gases such as carbon dioxide, carbon monoxide and sulphur into the atmosphere. Such gases can prove extremely poisonous. Volcanoes also emit large quantities of rock of varying sizes, e.g. ash, cinders and bombs. Such material is referred to as pyroclastic material.

Although lava flow is perhaps the most spectacular aspect of an eruption, it is generally too slow to result in any direct loss of life. Far more dangerous are the vast mudflows which can be triggered by volcanic activity. Such mudflows are known as lahars.

Lahars occur when volcanoes erupt within snow-capped mountains. The heat generated by the eruption melts the overlying snow, which results in the release of large amounts of water down slope. The water gathers up loose soil and trees on the lower slopes and the resulting mudslide can move at speeds of up to 160 km per hour.

Topic **3**
Seismic Activity: Earthquakes

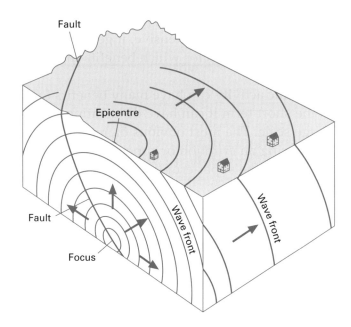

Figure 12 An earthquake

An **earthquake** can be said to be a vibration in the earth's crust caused by the sudden release of energy along a fault line beneath the earth's surface.

The **focus** of an earthquake is the place where energy in the form of **seismic waves** is first released. It lies some depth below the surface.

The **epicentre** of an earthquake is the point where the seismic waves first reach the surface. It lies directly above the focus.

Aftershocks refer to the smaller earthquakes which come after the initial, larger earthquake.

Seismographs are instruments used to measure the intensity of an earthquake.

The **Richter scale** is the scale used to classify the intensity of an earthquake. Each point on the Richter scale (1 to 10) represents an earthquake that is twice as powerful as the previous point.

The **Mercalli scale** is also used to classify the intensity of an earthquake. This scale measures earthquake intensity in terms of the visual damage it leads to. It is far less accurate than the Richter scale.

Causes of earthquakes

- **Elastic rebound** is the most common cause of earthquakes and occurs when rocks within the crust are subjected to pressure or stress. The rocks will bend or stretch in response to this pressure before eventually fracturing along a fault line causing an earthquake.
- Earthquakes can occur at the end of an ice age when the pressure of the overlying ice on the land is released. The crust rises in response to this release of pressure (**isostatic movement**) and as it does so it may stretch and fracture leading to an earthquake.
- Earthquakes can occur when groundwater (water seeping into the crust from the surface) seeps into and fills fractures in the crust. The pressure of the **subsurface water** as it fills the fracture can lead to a sudden further fracturing which causes an earthquake.
- Earthquakes can occur when **older faults** are reactivated. This may occur due to changes in convection currents in the mantle which cause a plate to move in a direction which it has not moved in for thousands of years.

Predicting an earthquake

The main ways of predicting an earthquake include:

- Using **strain meters** to measure the build-up of stresses in the earth's crust
- Using **tiltmeters** to measure the tilting or bulging of the land surface
- Using **satellite laser beams** to identify changes in the earth's magnetic field.

Limiting the damage

The main ways of limiting the damage which can be caused by an earthquake include:

- Encouraging strict **planning laws** to ensure buildings have adequate foundations
- Having a **national emergency plan** in place and practising it frequently
- Encouraging the use of shock absorbers and flexible materials in the **construction** of bridges and buildings.

> 1. Discuss how plate tectonics has increased our understanding of the global distribution of earthquakes.
>
> LQ   *Or*
>
> 'It is possible to predict where but not when earthquakes may occur.' Discuss this statement.

It is possible to predict where earthquakes will occur as they commonly take place at plate boundaries. They are especially common at destructive plate boundaries. They can occur where a continental plate collides with another continental plate but are more commonly found where an oceanic plate collides with a continental plate.

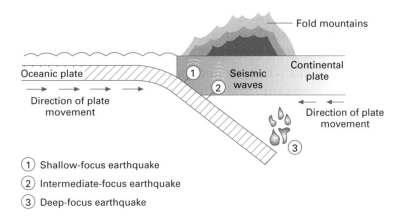

1. Shallow-focus earthquake
2. Intermediate-focus earthquake
3. Deep-focus earthquake

Figure 13 Earthquakes at destructive plate boundaries

As the plates collide, the heavier oceanic plate will subduct beneath the lighter continental plate. As the oceanic plate subducts, layers of rock are scraped off it by the continental plate to form mountains, e.g. the Rocky Mountains. However, as the plate subducts, it may become jammed against the continental plate. Convection currents will continue to attempt to move the oceanic plate downwards, which leads to a large build-up of pressure.

Eventually the pressure will become too great and the oceanic plate will break free suddenly, releasing energy/seismic waves which lead to an earthquake at the surface. It is difficult to predict when an earthquake will occur because it is impossible to tell when the pressure will become too great and lead to the fracturing of the crust.

If the energy is released close to the surface it is called a **shallow-focus earthquake**, if it occurs at a lower depth it is called an **intermediate-focus earthquake** and if it occurs at a significant depth it is called a **deep-focus earthquake**.

A second location where earthquakes commonly occur is at neutral/passive boundaries. Neutral/passive plate boundaries occur when plates are moving roughly parallel to each other. Such areas are usually free of volcanic activity but are extremely prone to seismic activity or earthquakes.

Figure 14 Earthquakes at neutral plate boundaries

As the plates are kilometres thick, the rocks within the plates tend to grind against each other as they slide past and the plates may become jammed. Convection currents will continue to push the plates in their respective directions which leads to a build-up of pressure and puts tremendous stress on the rocks within the plate.

These rocks can stretch up to a point (elastic rebound) but will eventually snap along a fault line. This is known as a transform fault. It releases seismic waves to the surface to cause an earthquake. The point at which the rocks snap is the focus of the earthquake. Again, it is impossible to predict when the rocks will snap and therefore it is very difficult to predict when an earthquake will take place.

An example of such activity can be seen along the San Andreas Fault, which lies between the North American plate (moving north-west at a rate of 1 cm per year) and the Pacific plate (moving in the same direction at a rate of 6 cm per year). Cities such as San Francisco and San Diego are affected by seismic activity along this line.

> **2.** **'Tsunami are powerful forces of nature and can have devastating**
> **LQ** **effects for coastal regions.' Discuss this statement with reference to a**
> **specific example you have studied.**

An example of a tsunami that I have studied is the **2004 South-East Asian tsunami**. This tsunami was caused by an earthquake on the ocean floor. Tsunami can also be the result of other natural forces such as volcanic eruptions on the ocean floor, large landslides or the impact of a meteor.

During an earthquake on the ocean floor the floor may be uplifted. If the ocean floor is uplifted by five meters, then a five-metre hump of

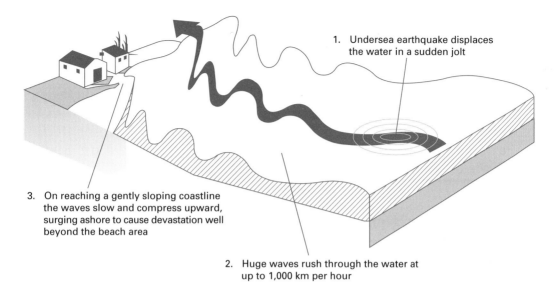

1. Undersea earthquake displaces the water in a sudden jolt

3. On reaching a gently sloping coastline the waves slow and compress upward, surging ashore to cause devastation well beyond the beach area

2. Huge waves rush through the water at up to 1,000 km per hour

Figure 15 A tsunami

excess water is created at the surface. When this excess hump of water collapses it creates a succession of waves in either direction. These waves can be 100–500 km in length and can move across the ocean at speeds of 800–1,000 km per hour.

As the wave approaches the coastline, the front of the wave slows down in the shallow water. However, the back of the wave continues to move at full speed causing it to double up over the front of the wave, thus increasing its speed and force as it hits the coastline.

On 26 December 2004 an earthquake measuring 8.5 on the Richter scale (the largest in forty years) took place on the floor of the Indian Ocean. The Indian and Burma plates had pressed against each other until the lighter Burma plate suddenly shot upwards, displacing the water by about 10 m at the surface. This movement released energy equivalent to 10,000 atomic bombs. The tsunami generated by this created waves 160 km long and 15 m high.

Although South-East Asia was worst affected, areas as far away as Somalia (5,000 km) were also hit. Indonesia was worst affected and was hit with three tsunami in three minutes. Thailand was also devastated. Islands such as Trinket were split in two while other islands disappeared completely. In all, over 170,000 people were killed.

As well as the obvious and devastating short-term effects of the tsunami, the region has also suffered significant long-term negative effects from an economic perspective. Tourism, the lifeblood of the economy, has suffered greatly as tourist numbers declined significantly in the aftermath of the tsunami.

LQ **3. Discuss the effects which a major earthquake has had on any one city you have studied.**

An example of an earthquake that I have studied is the **1985 Mexico City earthquake**. This was one of the most devastating earthquakes in the history of the Americas.

On Thursday 19 September 1985, at 7.19 a.m., Mexico City was stuck by an earthquake which measured 8.1 on the Richter scale. The epicentre of the quake was off the Pacific coast of Mexico, roughly 350 km from the city. The earthquake would be felt as far away as Los Angeles. As a result of the earthquake at least 9,000 people were killed, 30,000 injured and almost 100,000 left homeless; 416 buildings were destroyed and over 3,000 more were seriously damaged.

The cause of the earthquake was tectonic movement of plates. Mexico City is close to a destructive plate boundary between the Cocos plate and the North American plate. As the Cocos plate subducted beneath the North American plate, the friction created caused the Cocos plate to slip suddenly, which led to the release of energy, which in turn caused the earthquake.

Although the epicentre was more than 300 km away, Mexico City suffered the most damage. Tremors from the quake lasted for three or four minutes and were felt over an area of 825,000 km^2. The most damaged areas were on the bed of the historic Lake Texcoco. Building damage was worsened by the damp soils which caused the foundations of buildings to become less stable.

The excessive damage was attributed in part to poor enforcement of building codes and the lack of deep foundations in many of Mexico City's buildings. The water and sewage systems were destroyed during the earthquake, which contaminated the city's water supply. Electricity lines were destroyed, which sparked many fires. Although official statistics state that 3,000 people died, independent estimates are much higher and many believe that the death toll reached 60,000.

There were also significant aftershocks to the earthquake. Thirty-six hours after the initial tremors an earthquake measuring 7.5 on the Richter scale shook the city causing widespread panic.

The long-term effects of the earthquake on the city have been significant. Large-scale emigration followed the earthquake. In an attempt to prevent further disasters in the future, the government funded a state-of-the-art detection system that sends early warning messages to Mexico City. The success of this system is shown by the fact that an earthquake in 1999, which measured 7.4 on the Richter scale, only claimed one life.

Topic 4
Folding and Faulting

Folding

Folding of the earth's crust occurs at destructive boundaries when plates, which were originally flat, collide, causing them to buckle or wrinkle. This often leads to the formation of fold mountains. Folding is best observed when sedimentary rocks are affected as the layers of folded rock are clearly visible.

There are three **types of fold**.

- Simple/symmetrical fold
- Asymmetrical fold
- Overfold

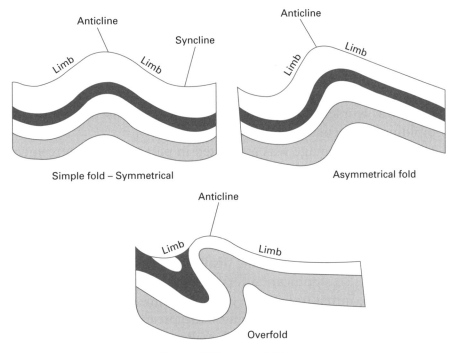

Figure 16 Types of folding

The **anticline** is the upward part of the fold or the arch.
The **syncline** is the downward part of the fold or the trough.
Limbs are the arms or sides of the fold.

Faulting

Faulting occurs when rocks within the earth's crust are subjected to pressure or stress. Rocks can only withstand pressure up to a point before they develop fractures. If this fracturing involves movement of the land it is called a geological fault.

There are three **types of fault**.

- Normal fault
- Reverse fault
- Tear fault

Normal fault	Reverse fault	Tear fault
Tension in the crust	Also called thrust fault	Also called transform fault
↓	↓	↓
Occurs at constructive plate boundaries	Compression in the crust	Occurs at neutral plate boundaries
↓	↓	↓
Tension leads to stretching of crust	Compression causes folding of crust	Pressure is exerted on opposite ends of crust
↓	↓	↓
Stretching leads to thinning of rocks	Folding leads to crust fracturing along the anticline	Shearing of crust occurs
↓		↓
Eventually the rocks fracture along a fault line	↓	Eventually the rocks fracture along a fault line
↓		↓
Movement of land is downwards	**Movement of land is upwards**	**Movement of land is horizontal**
↓	↓	↓
Example is Kingscourt, Co. Cavan	Example is Killarney–Mallow Fault	Example is the San Andreas Fault, USA

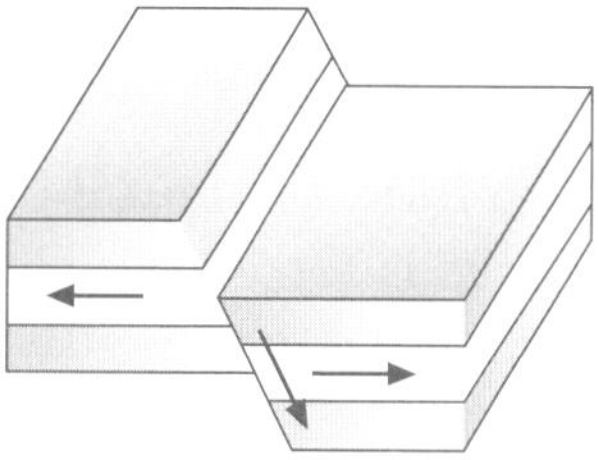 **Figure 17** Normal fault	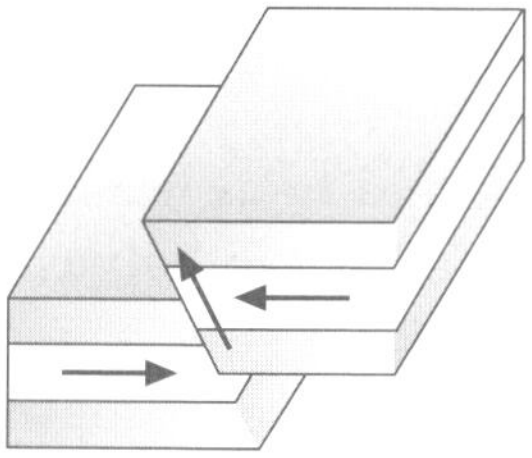 **Figure 18** Reverse fault	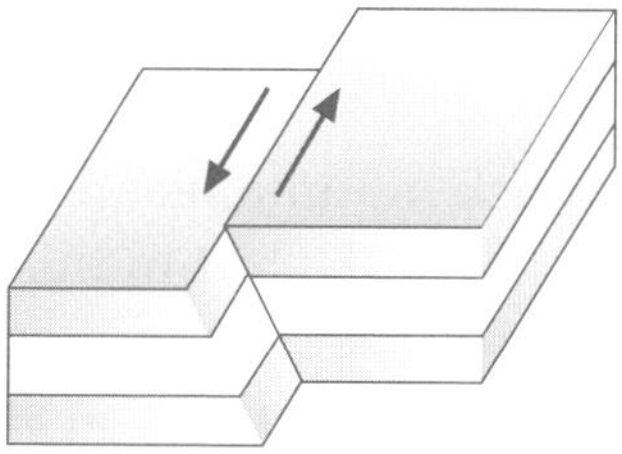 **Figure 19** Tear fault

A **scarp** (also know as an escarpment) refers to the cliff which occurs as a result of the vertical displacement of the rock.

Throw is the amount of vertical displacement or height of the scarp.

Heave is the amount of horizontal displacement of the rock.

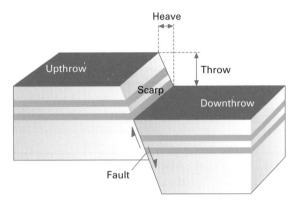

Figure 20 Characteristics of a fault

Block mountains and rift valleys (horst and graben)

Rift valleys are also referred to as graben. They occur when a section of the earth's crust slips downwards between two parallel fault lines. The fault lines can be hundreds of kilometres apart and the valley that is produced can be immense with large escarpments at either side. Examples include the Rhine Rift Valley in Germany and Death Valley in the USA.

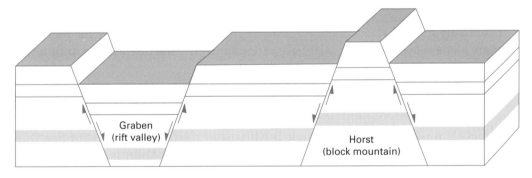

Figure 21 Block mountains and rift valleys

Block mountains are also referred to as horst. They also form as a result of parallel faults but in this case the land in between the faults is forced upwards due to compression at either side. The mountain that subsequently forms can be blocky in structure but is eventually shaped by the processes of weathering and erosion. Such mountains can also form when the land either side of parallel faults is downthrown. Examples of block mountains include the Ox Mountains in Ireland and the Black Forest Mountains in Germany.

LQ **1. Discuss the evidence to suggest that Ireland was close to a plate boundary in the past.**

It is obvious that Ireland was close to a plate boundary in the past given the presence of many features produced by fold movement across the country. Examples of these features include the mountain ranges formed during the **Caledonian fold movement**.

The Caledonian fold movement took place 400 million years ago following the closure of the Iapetus Sea and the collision of the American and Eurasian plates. Following that collision a period of intensive mountain building took place which lasted for roughly 50 million years, with land on both sides of the collision affected.

The mountain ranges formed in Ireland in this period, such as the Nephin Beg Mountains and Maumturk Mountains in Connacht, would have been as high as the present-day Pyrenees. The mountains have been worn down to their present size by 400 million years of weathering and erosion. Because of the direction the plates were travelling, the folds have an almost north–south trend. Many of the region's rivers now flow through the synclines of the fold, for example the River Corrib and the River Shannon.

Further evidence that Ireland was close to a plate boundary in the past are the many features of fold movement in Munster. These show that Ireland was once close to a destructive plate boundary. The **Amorican fold movement** took place 250 million years ago following a collision between the Eurasian and African plates. This collision did not create mountains in Ireland as large as the Caledonian fold movement did because this time Ireland was much further away from the point of collision.

The part of Ireland that was most affected was the Munster region and it was in this period that the Munster ridge and valley province was formed. During this period of plate collision, layers of sedimentary rocks such as limestone and sandstone were folded upwards to form the present-day Macgillycuddy's Reeks. Rivers such as the Bandon and the Blackwater now flow through the synclines of the Amorican folds.

The following paragraph is not part of the answer to the above question but you must know it in order to be able to answer certain short questions on folding.

The third main period of fold mountain construction in the earth's history is the recent **Alpine fold movement** which did not affect Ireland. This occurred only 60 million years ago when the African plate again collided with the Eurasian plate. Mountain ranges such as the Alps and the Apennines were formed in this period. Other mountain ranges formed around this time, although not from the same plate collision, include the Himalayas and the Andes.

LQ 2. Discuss the extent to which folding and faulting have shaped the Irish landscape.

It is obvious that folding and faulting have shaped the Irish landscape given the presence of so many features associated with these processes.

Fold movement is responsible for many of Ireland's mountain ranges. Ireland's oldest mountain ranges were formed during the Caledonian fold movement over 400 million years ago. This occurred due to a collision between the American plate and the Eurasian plate. The collision caused large parts of Connacht and Leinster to buckle and wrinkle and led to the formation of the Nephin Beg Mountains and Maumturk Mountains in the west, and the Dublin and Wicklow Mountains and the Leinster batholith in the east. These mountains would have been as big as the present-day Alps but have been worn down to their present size by the processes of weathering and erosion.

The second way in which folding shaped Ireland's landscape occurred during the Amorican fold movement over 250 million years ago. This was caused by a collision between the African and Eurasian plates. Ireland was further away from the point of collision than it was during the Caledonian folding so the mountains formed in Ireland in this period were smaller. Macgillycuddy's Reeks were formed in this period as was the Munster ridge and valley province. Today rivers such as the Blackwater and the Lee flow through the synclines of this fold.

Faulting has also shaped the Irish landscape. Faulting is said to occur when rocks are subjected to pressure and stress causing them to fracture along a fault line. If movement of land subsequently occurs it is known as faulting. There are numerous fault lines found across Ireland.

The first type of fault found in Ireland is a normal fault, which occurs when rocks within the crust are subjected to tension at constructive plate boundaries. This in turn leads to stretching and thinning of the rock. Eventually the rock fractures and the movement of land is downwards. An example of this type of fault can be seen near Kingscourt, Co. Cavan.

The second type of fault found in Ireland is a reverse fault. This occurs when rocks within the crust are subjected to compression at destructive plate boundaries. This compression causes the rocks to fold upwards. The rocks can only fold up to a certain point before they fracture along the anticline. The subsequent movement of land is upwards. An example of this fault can be seen running from Killarney to Mallow.

Faulting can also lead to the formation of block mountains, e.g. the Ox Mountains in Connacht. Such mountains formed when the land between two parallel faults was forced upwards. It is obvious therefore that the processes of folding and faulting have played a major role in shaping the Irish landscape.

Topic 5
The Rock Cycle

The rocks of the world are continually being formed, modified, destroyed and reconstructed.

- **Formed**: this occurs when rising magma cools either within the crust or on the surface to form **igneous rocks**.
- **Modified**: this occurs when rocks are subjected to great heat or pressure and change characteristics as a result to form **metamorphic rocks**.
- **Destroyed**: this occurs when rocks at the surface are broken into smaller sediments by the processes of **weathering** and **erosion**.
- **Reconstructed**: this occurs when sediments are compressed together to form solid rocks called **sedimentary rocks**.

Igneous rocks

Igneous rocks are formed when magma from the mantle upwells and cools either within the crust or on the surface.

There are two **types of igneous rocks**.

- **Intrusive/plutonic rocks** are formed when magma from the mantle is forced up into the overlying crust but does not reach the surface. Instead it cools and solidifies to form rocks such as granite within the crust.
- **Extrusive/volcanic rocks** are formed when magma is forced up from the mantle, through the crust, and reaches the surface as lava where it cools to form rocks such as basalt.

Example of intrusive rock formation: Granite

Granite rocks are formed when magma cools very slowly within the earth's crust. They are composed of three minerals: mica, feldspar and quartz. The percentages of these minerals vary, which creates granites of different colours. The dominant colour of granite is grey. Granites are strong, resistant rocks and are commonly used as a building material. When granite is broken down by weathering it produces clay.

Much of Ireland's granite was formed during the Caledonian fold movement 400 million years ago. Examples in Ireland include the Dublin and Wicklow Mountains, the Donegal Mountains and the Leinster batholith.

Example of extrusive rock formation: Basalt

Basalt makes up almost 90 per cent of all extrusive rocks. It is formed when lava is exposed to air and cools and solidifies rapidly to form a black or dark grey coloured rock that has small crystals. Basalt is a hard rock which makes it suitable as a material for road construction, while its dull colour makes it unsuitable as a building material. When basalt weathers it produces a deep fertile soil, as is found in Brazil. Basalt commonly forms features such as plateaux when it flows onto the surface through fissures (cracks) in the earth's crust.

Examples can be found in the Antrim–Derry plateau in Ireland and in Auvergne in France.

Sedimentary rocks

Sedimentary rocks are formed when igneous or metamorphic rocks are exposed to weathering and erosion. These processes break the rocks into smaller particles. The particles/sediments are then transported elsewhere by wind, water or ice. The deposited sediments accumulate on top of each other and are compressed by their own weight to form sedimentary rocks.

There are two **types of sedimentary rocks**.

- Inorganic sedimentary rocks
- Organic sedimentary rocks

Example of an inorganic sedimentary rock: Sandstone

Sandstone is the second most common rock type in Ireland. It consists of grains of sand which were deposited on land or in water and later cemented together. **Old red sandstone** (ORS) has a characteristic brown/red colour because of the presence of iron oxide. Ireland's ORS was laid down around 400 million years ago when Ireland had a desert climate and weathering and erosion were breaking down the newly formed Caledonian fold mountains.

Examples in Ireland include the Comeragh Mountains, Co. Waterford; Macgillycuddy's Reeks, Co. Kerry; and Rush, Co. Dublin.

Example of organic sedimentary rock: Limestone

The formation of limestone is dealt with in Topic 8.

Metamorphic rocks

Metamorphic rocks are rocks which were once either igneous or sedimentary rocks but which have been changed into a new rock due to great heat or pressure.

There are two ways in which metamorphic rocks can form.

- **Thermal metamorphism** occurs due to heat alone when magma melts its way into the crust and 'cooks' the rocks which are close to it.
- **Regional metamorphism** occurs due to both heat and pressure over a very large area. This usually occurs during fold mountain construction.

Examples of changes in rocks due to metamorphism		
Granite (igneous)	$\longrightarrow$	Gneiss
Limestone (sedimentary)	$\longrightarrow$	Marble
Shale (sedimentary)	$\longrightarrow$	Slate
Sandstone (sedimentary)	$\longrightarrow$	Quartzite

Characteristics of a metamorphic rock: Marble

Marble is a metamorphic rock which forms when limestone is exposed to great heat or pressure. Marble exists in different colours: white, green, red and black. There are many factors which determine the colour of marble such as the intensity of the heat and pressure to which the limestone was exposed, and the purity or calcium content of the limestone. Limestone which contains a high percentage of calcium carbonate can produce pure white marble, which is quite rare. Marble has many uses, most notably for sculpture and interior decoration.

Examples of marble can be found in Carrera, Italy (white) as well as Marble Arch upland in Co. Fermanagh.

LQ 1. Discuss one way in which humans have interacted with the rock cycle.

An example of human interaction in the rock cycle which I have studied is **oil and gas exploration in the North Sea.** Humans have interacted with the rock cycle in the North Sea since the discovery of natural gas at Slochteren in the Netherlands in 1961. The geological formations of the gas field gave rise to the belief that both oil and gas could be found within the earth's crust beneath the North Sea.

The Continental Shelf Act 1964 divided the North Sea into sections for exploitation between the countries that bordered it and greatly benefited Britain and Norway. Britain was especially anxious to develop any hydrocarbon deposits and its successful exploration was a major factor in changing its domestic energy market. Large-scale increases in Britain's production of oil and natural gas between 1970 and 1990 resulted in dependency levels on imported energy declining significantly.

In contrast to the British, the Norwegians proceeded more cautiously in exploiting their oil and gas reserves in the North Sea. In 1969 the Norwegians discovered oil at Ekofisk and this was followed by further finds at the Sleipner field as well as the gas fields of Frigg and Cod. By the mid-1980s this successful interaction with the rock cycle meant that oil equalled hydroelectric power (HEP) in supplying Norway's energy needs. The Norwegian government controls exploitation through a state-owned company called Statoil and another called Hydro. This strategy ensures that most of the profits go directly to the state.

Throughout this interaction with the geology of the ocean floor numerous problems have been encountered. Unlike most countries, Norway exports its oil and gas directly from the production platforms. This is due to the presence of a 200-metre oceanic trench which prevented oil and gas being piped back to Norway for refinement. This problem was overcome in the 1980s and has led to employment in the refining sector in towns such as Bergen and Stavanger.

Exports of oil and gas have played a vital part in financing Norway's booming economy. Because of its supplies of HEP, Norway can export 80 per cent of its oil and gas, which brings in foreign revenue. The 140 wells drilled in the Norwegian sector of the North Sea have provided over 5,000 jobs directly with a further 20,000 people employed indirectly in related industries on shore. The Norwegian government proceeded carefully in its exploitation of North Sea oil and gas and it is estimated that Norwegian reserves will last well into the 2200s.

It is also estimated that significant deposits lie in the Norwegian sector north of 62°N which has yet to be exploited. The reluctance of the Norwegian government to sanction this is due to the importance of the fishing industry in the region and the damage an oil spill would have on this sector. Norway's exploitation of its oil and gas reserves provides a good example of successful human interaction with the rock cycle.

LQ 2. Discuss the formation of any one igneous rock and show how that rock type can produce a distinctive landscape.

The igneous rock I have studied is **granite**. Granite rocks are formed when magma cools very slowly deep within the earth's crust.

Granite is composed of three minerals: mica, feldspar and quartz (silica). Feldspar and quartz are usually the dominant minerals. The relative percentages of these minerals can vary greatly and produce granites of different colours. Although granites can range in colour from black to white, their dominant colour is grey. Granites are strong, resistant rocks and are commonly used as a building material.

Most of Ireland's granites were formed during the Caledonian and Amorican fold movements, i.e. at destructive plate boundaries. When two plates collide, the heavier plate is subducted beneath the lighter one. As this subducting plate descends into the mantle it begins to melt at a depth of almost 80 km. This melting sends plumes of magma upwards toward the overlying plate. The magma melts into the overlying plate and melts the rocks within it. When the magma cools, it forms an intrusive/plutonic rock such as granite.

Granite produces a distinctive landscape as it forms intrusive features such as sills, dykes and batholiths. A dyke is produced when a vertical plume of magma is injected up into a fracture in the crust. The pressure of the magma widens the fracture. Eventually the magma will cool to form a vertical sheet of granite called a dyke.

Sills occur when magma is injected horizontally between layers of sedimentary rock close to the surface. Again the magma will melt the surrounding rock before cooling to form a horizontal layer of granite called a sill. If the magma pushes the overlying rock upwards a laccolith sill forms and if the magma pushes the underlying rock down a loppolith sill is formed.

Batholiths are formed when magma from the mantle is forced into the crust where it cools and solidifies to form granite. Batholiths occur on a much larger scale than sills and can be over 30 km deep and hundreds of kilometres wide. Batholiths do not occur when magma seeps into the crust through fractures but when enormous amounts of magma simply push up into the crust and melt the denser rocks therein.

Batholiths can be exposed at the surface when the overlying layers of rocks are removed by denudation (weathering and erosion). They can also be exposed to the surface when plates collide and buckle the crust forming fold mountains. The Leinster batholith runs for 120 km from Dublin to Kilkenny and was brought to the surface during the Caledonian fold movement 400 million years ago, which formed the Dublin and Wicklow mountains.

Diagram-based questions on the rock cycle

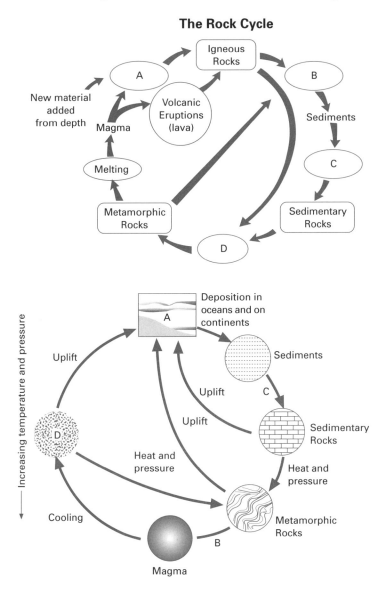

Figure 22 Diagram-based questions on the rock cycle

For the above type of question you will be asked to write a brief description of what is occuring at points A, B, C and D.

Weathering is the process whereby rocks on the surface are broken down or decay. Weathering does not involve the removal of the material that results.

There are three **types of weathering**.

- Mechanical weathering
- Chemical weathering
- Biological weathering

Mechanical weathering

Mechanical weathering is the breakdown of rock into smaller particles by physical processes.

There are four **types of mechanical weathering**.

- Free-thaw action
- Exfoliation
- Pressure release
- Salt crystallisation

Freeze-thaw action commonly occurs in temperate climates where temperatures fluctuate above and below 0°C. This process is especially effective on exposed rocks which contain cracks, joints and fractures. During warmer temperatures precipitation causes water to accumulate in these cracks. During colder temperatures the water may freeze and, as a result, may

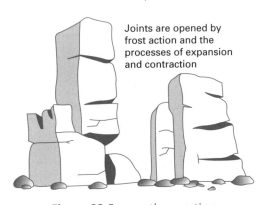

Joints are opened by frost action and the processes of expansion and contraction

Figure 23 Freeze-thaw action

expand by up to 10 per cent. This expansion puts pressure on the surrounding rocks, parts of which may break off as a result. These small particles which break off are called **scree.**

Exfoliation is also known as onion weathering. This process is common in areas in which there is a large diurnal range of temperature (i.e. a big difference between day and night temperatures). This process therefore is effective in desert/arid climates where rocks are exposed at the surface. The intense day-time heat causes the outer layer of the rock to expand, while the cold night-time temperatures cause the layer to contract. This process may continue for decades but eventually the continued expansion and contraction causes the outer layer of the rock to break off, forming scree.

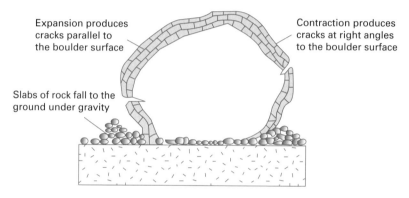

Figure 24 Exfoliation

Pressure release occurs when rocks such as granite have formed under great pressure from overlying rocks. As the overlying rocks are removed by denudation (weathering and erosion), the pressure on the granite is gradually released. As this pressure is being released the granite rises slowly (isostatic movement). As the mass of granite rises it fractures and cracks leaving it open and vulnerable to other forms of weathering when it reaches the surface.

Salt crystallisation is common in tropical climates where periods of heavy rainfall are followed by intense heat. This process occurs when water carrying a high sodium (salt) content seeps into the cracks and joints of rocks. If the water then evaporates, the remaining salt crystals will expand leading to the breakdown of the rock.

Chemical weathering

Chemical weathering is the breakdown of minerals within the rock. Moisture is essential for chemical weathering to occur.

There are four **types of chemical weathering**.

- Oxidation
- Hydration
- Hydrolysis
- Carbonation

Oxidation occurs when water seeps into rocks that have a high content of iron oxide. An example of a rock type which contains iron oxide is old red sandstone. The oxygen in the water reacts with the iron minerals, rusting them, which in turn leads to the breakdown of the rock.

Hydration occurs when minerals which are moisture deficient are exposed to large amounts of water. The water causes the minerals to expand rapidly, which shatters the rock.

Hydrolysis occurs when water seeps into rocks and the hydrogen in the water reacts with a mineral in the rock which leads to the breakdown of the rock.

Carbonation is the process whereby rainwater dissolves soluble rocks such as limestone. As rainwater falls it reacts with carbon dioxide in the atmosphere to form a weak carbonic acid. This acid reacts with the calcium carbonate in the limestone to form calcium bicarbonate, which is easily washed away.

Biological weathering

Biological weathering occurs when the earth's surface is broken down by plants, animals and humans. Biological weathering is the least effective of the three types of weathering.

Plants can help to break down surface rocks through their root structure.

Animals can break down surface rocks as a result of burrowing. The actions of birds can break down rocks on cliffs in coastal regions.

Humans contribute to the weathering of rocks in a number of ways such as quarrying, mining, and oil and gas exploration.

Factors which affect the amount of weathering in a region

- **Climate** determines the dominant type of weathering in a region. For example desert climates experience exfoliation most regularly, upland climates are prone to freeze-thaw action, and temperate climates are susceptible to chemical weathering.

- **Rock type** can influence the rate of weathering in a region. Sedimentary rocks such as limestone are especially vulnerable to weathering as they contain numerous joints and fractures which allow water to accumulate and seep into the rocks.
- **Time** – although the rate of weathering may vary from place to place, all rocks are eventually broken down.

Topic 7
Mass Movement

Mass movement is the process by which weathered material such as soil, stones, rock and mud moves downhill due to the force of gravity and is eventually carried away by other agents.

Mass movements can be fast or slow, and wet or dry.

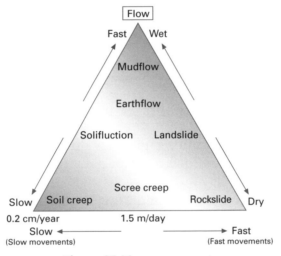

Figure 25 Mass movements

LQ 1. **Discuss the development of any one slow and one fast mass movement.**

Soil creep is the slowest form of mass movement but also the most common. It involves the steady movement of soil or weathered rock particles down slope. This type of movement is difficult to observe as it occurs at a rate of about 0.5 cm per year. Soil creep may only become apparent when posts, fences or trees are first tilted and then displaced downhill. On short slopes, a stepped pattern may develop across the slope. These slopes are called terracettes. The material that is moving down slope is referred to as the regolith. Vegetation reduces soil creep as the roots of plants such as grasses and trees bind the soil particles together.

Mudflows are an example of fast mass movement. They can occur when torrential rain seeps into deep soils on a steep slope. The soil can quickly become saturated, particularly if the underlying rock is

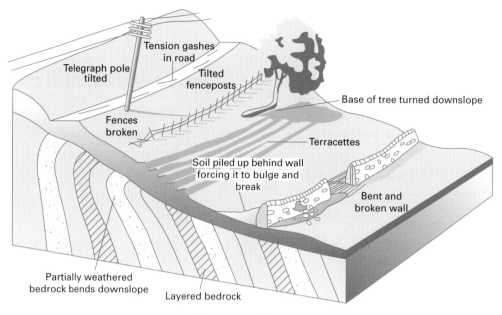

Figure 26 Soil creep

impermeable. This results in a rapid flow down slope of unconsolidated soil, rock and mud. Mudflows are especially common in soils which have a high percentage of clay.

The most dangerous form of mudflow is a **lahar**. Lahars commonly occur on snow-capped volcanic peaks. If there is a volcanic eruption, the lava that is emitted will melt the overlying snow, releasing vast quantities of water. As this water moves quickly to the lower slopes, which are not covered with snow, it gathers loose material such as soils and rocks to form a mudflow moving at up to 100 km per hour. Mount St Helens in the USA has caused numerous lahars, most notably in 1980.

Other forms of mass movement

Rotational slumping

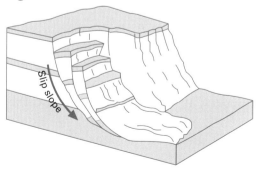

Figure 27 Rotational slumping

Rock fall

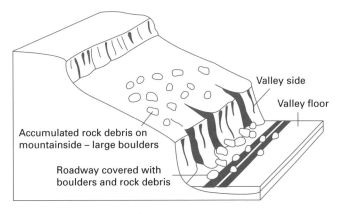

Figure 28 Rockslide

Debris avalanche

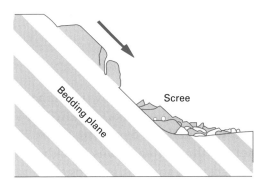

Figure 29 Debris avalanche

Bog bursts

Bog bursts occur when blanket bogs absorb excess amounts of precipitation. If the bog lies on sloping ground there may be a slow or fast movement of the bog down slope which will leave a concave scar where the bog used to lie and a large mound where it ended up.

Topic **8**
Karst Landscapes: Limestone Regions

The most likely long questions you will be asked concerning limestone or karst regions are as follows.

LQ **1.** Discuss the formation of any one sedimentary rock you have studied and show how it produces a distinctive landscape.

LQ **2.** Discuss any two features (surface or subsurface) formed by the process of chemical weathering.

In order to answer such questions there are three things you need to know:

* The formation of limestone
* The relevant process of chemical weathering (carbonation)
* Features of limestone which produce a distinctive landscape.

Formation of limestone

Limestone is a sedimentary rock. Such rocks tend to form when sediments accumulate, are compressed under their own weight and solidify to form rock in a process known as **lithification**.

Most of the world's limestone formed on the floors of tropical oceans near the equator. The oceans contained vast amounts of large and small organisms which fell to the sea floor when they died. Once there they either lay as bones and shells or were eroded into a thick mud by the actions of the waves. When large amounts of this material gathered on the floor it was compressed by the weight of the water to form solid limestone.

Ireland's limestone was formed roughly 350 million years ago when Ireland was located near the equator. In this period the only part of Ireland which stood above sea level was the newly formed Caledonian fold mountains. The remainder of the country was submerged in a shallow tropical ocean and a large amount of limestone formed on what is now the surface. The limestone formed in Ireland in this period is known as **Carboniferous limestone**.

Chemical weathering: Carbonation

Limestone can be dissolved by rainwater in a form of chemical weathering called carbonation. When rainwater falls it mixes with carbon dioxide in the atmosphere to form a weak carbonic acid. When this acid subsequently falls on limestone it reacts with the calcium carbonate in the limestone to form calcium bicarbonate. Calcium bicarbonate is liquid and is easily washed away.

Rainwater + carbon dioxide = carbonic acid + calcium carbonate = calcium bicarbonate
$$H_2O \qquad CO_2 \qquad H_2CO_3 \qquad CaCO_3 \qquad Ca[HCO_3]_2$$

Distinctive features of limestone regions

Limestone pavements are a distinctive feature found in karst regions which form as a result of the process of chemical weathering known as carbonation. They form when the protective overlying layers of soil and vegetation are removed, usually by glacial erosion, exposing the limestone at the surface.

Limestone consists of vertical joints and horizontal bedding planes. Where the joints reach the surface they represent lines of weakness and are the first part of the rock to be attacked by carbonation. This results in small gashes forming in the rock.

These gashes gather rainfall, which increases the amount of carbonation taking place. This in turn deepens the gashes which are now termed **grikes**. The flat slabs of limestone that separate grikes are called **clints**. A combination of clints and grikes is known as a limestone pavement.

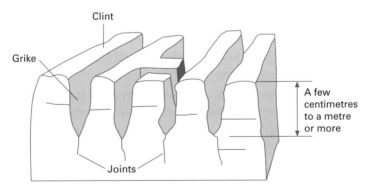

Figure 30 A limestone pavement

The clints are also weathered by carbonation, albeit at a much slower rate. Evidence of this weathering can be found in the many small hollows called **karren** which can be observed on the clints.

Small pockets of soil may develop in sheltered grikes, which in turn become home to polar and tropical plant types such as the blue gentian and mountain avens.

Examples of limestone pavements can be seen at Black Head and the Burren, Co. Clare; Marble Arch upland in Co. Fermanagh; and in Kentucky, USA.

Swallow holes or **sink holes** are also referred to as **sluggas**. A swallow hole is an opening in the bed of a river which allows the river to disappear underground where it then continues on its course at a lower level. Such holes can occur in a number of ways.

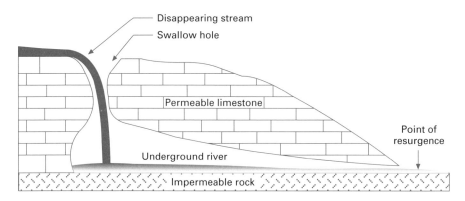

Figure 31 A swallow hole

Swallow holes commonly form when an area of impermeable rock such as shale meets an area of permeable rock such as limestone. The initial cause of a swallow hole is groundwater. This is water which seeps into the cracks and joints of the pervious (i.e. allows water to pass through) limestone and continues to seep downwards until it reaches a layer of impermeable rock. Because the water cannot pass through the impermeable rock it accumulates above it and saturates the overlying rock.

This saturated rock is eventually dissolved by the carbonic acid in the water, thus forming hundreds of kilometres of underground tunnels. Swallow holes form when the roofs of these tunnels collapse and a river that had been flowing on the surface plunges through the hole and flows underground through the pre-existing tunnels. As the rivers flow through the tunnels they may enlarge them in places forming caves/caverns. Swallow holes usually have the shape of an inverted cone. Rivers which disappear underground may later reappear at the surface. The point at which they reappear is known as the point of resurgence.

Examples of such features include Poll an Phuca in the Burren, Co. Clare and Poll na mbunny, Co. Mayo.

Dripstone features form in underground caves in limestone regions. Underground caves form when a river disappears underground through a swallow hole and continues through pre-existing tunnels which were formed by groundwater. As the rivers flow through these tunnels they can erode the weaker parts of the limestone to form caves or caverns. Within these caves, dripstone features form.

Dripstone features occur when water seeps down through the pervious limestone and mixes with the calcium carbonate in the limestone. This mixture will continue to seep downwards until it meets the roof of a cave, which it then drips into through cracks in the cave roof. As it drips into the cave, evaporation takes place and a small amount of calcium carbonate (calcite) is left on the cave roof.

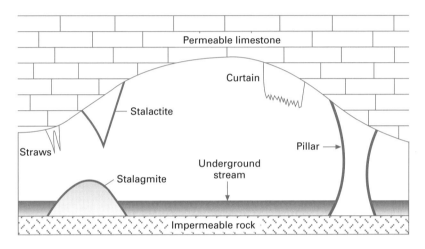

Figure 32 Dripstone features

In areas of constant seepage this calcite will grow downwards to form a stalactite. On the floor of the cave a stalagmite forms in the same way when the water splashes on the floor. When stalactites and stalagmites join they form a pillar or column. When water seeps into the cave through narrow fissures a curtain is formed. In areas of intermittent seepage straws will form.

Dripstone features are made from calcite, which in its purist form is white. However, due to impurities in rainwater the features tend to be brownish-yellow in colour.

Examples of these features can be seen in Aillwee Cave, Co. Clare; Crag Cave, Co. Kerry; and Jenolan Caves near Sydney in Australia.

A **turlough** is a temporary lake found in karst regions. It occurs due to changes in the water table in areas where there is a depression in the landscape. In winter, when the water table rises, a lake forms in the depression. In summer, when the water table falls, the lake is dry.

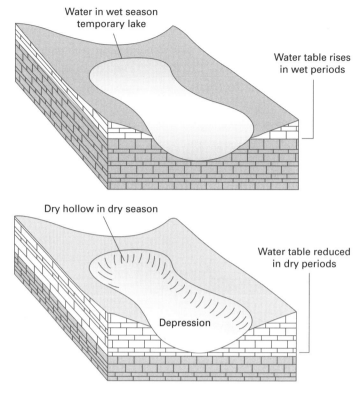

Figure 33 Turloughs

A **dry valley** occurs when a river disappears underground through a swallow hole and no longer flows through the valley which it had previously created by means of vertical erosion.

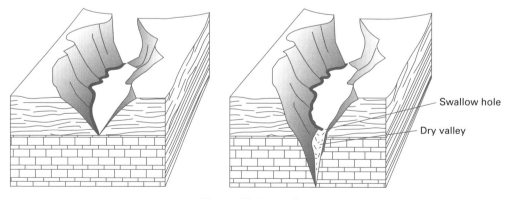

Figure 34 Dry valley

Dolines/polje/uavala are depressions in a limestone region of varying size.

Topic 9
Rivers/Fluvial Landscapes

River stages

Rivers have three stages: youthful, mature and old.

Youthful stage/upper course
- Steep gradient
- Fast-flowing water
- Vertical erosion of the river bed
- Valley is steep sided

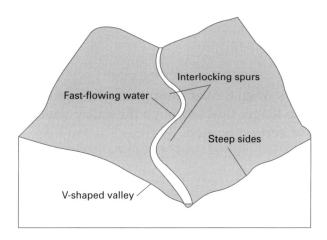

Figure 35 Stages of a river: youth

Mature stage/middle course
- Gradient is less steep
- Water is slowing down
- Lateral erosion of the river banks
- Deposition also takes place
- River is transporting a heavy load

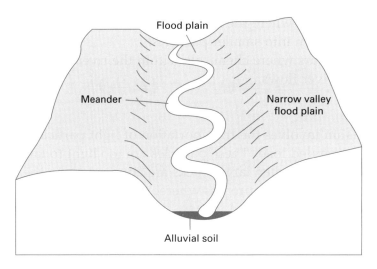

Figure 36 Stages of a river: maturity

Old stage/lower course
- Gradient is very gentle
- Deposition is the main process
- Valley is wide and flat

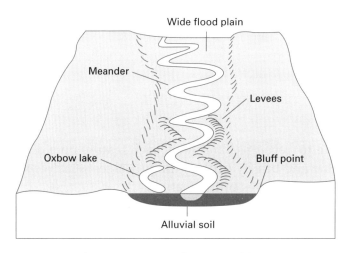

Figure 37 Stages of a river: old age

Processes of river erosion
- **Hydraulic action** is the power and force of moving water. It is most effective on bends.
- **Abrasion** is where the river uses its **load** (the material it is carrying) to erode its bed and banks.

- **Attrition** occurs where the rocks within the load crash against each other and break down into smaller particles.
- **Solution** occurs where chemicals within the river dissolve the rocks over which the river flows.

Processes of river transportation

- **Suspension** involves the transportation of light particles such as sand and silt in suspended load. These particles are too light to fall to the river bed.
- **Saltation** occurs when larger rocks are bounced along the river bed.
- **Bottom traction** is the process whereby larger rocks are simply rolled slowly along the river bed.
- **Solution** is the process whereby rocks which have been dissolved are carried as minerals within the river.

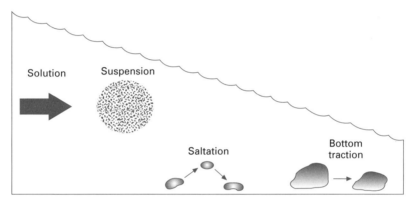

Figure 38 Processes of river transportation

Fluvial features

You must be able to: recognise and label each feature on a diagram or photograph, name and briefly explain the processes which led to its formation and give examples of the feature.

V-shaped valleys are found in the youthful stage of a river as a result of vertical erosion of the river bed. The processes which lead to their formation include hydraulic action, abrasion, attrition and solution. Weathering also takes place on the valley sides and helps to provide the river with a load (material carried by a river).

When a river encounters patches of hard rock which it cannot erode it simply flows around them. These bands of hard rock which project into the valley from either side are known as **interlocking spurs.**

Examples of V-shaped valleys include the Upper Erriff in Co. Mayo and the Devil's Glen in Co. Wicklow.

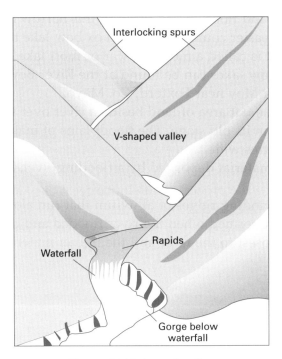

Figure 39 V-shaped valley

Ox-bow lakes are features found in the mature and mainly old stages of a river. They are formed by the processes of lateral erosion (hydraulic action, abrasion, attrition, solution) and deposition.

Ox-bow lakes occur when a meander becomes very pronounced and the opposite ends of the meander migrate towards each other. This leaves a narrow neck of land between the two. The river will eventually (usually in

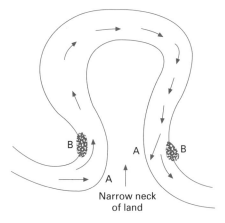

At a pronounced meander erosion takes place at (A) and deposition takes place at (B)

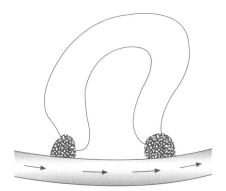

The river breaks through the narrow neck of land and leaves the ox-bow lake to one side

Figure 40 Formation of an ox-bow lake

times of heavy rain and flood) break through this narrow neck and continue on a straighter and easier course, leaving an ox bow lake to one side. If the ox bow lake dries up it is called a meander scar or mort lake.

Examples of ox-bow lakes can be found at the River Boyne near Slane, Co. Meath and the River Moy near Foxford, Co. Mayo.

A **floodplain** is the flat area of land beside a river over which a river floods, particularly in its old stage. The floodplains of major rivers can be hundreds of kilometres wide.

Alluvium is the material deposited by a flooding river. Alluvium tends to be very fertile.

Levees are low, winding ridges of alluvium that run alongside a river in its old stage. They were formed when the river flooded and deposited the heaviest material closest to the river and the lighter material further away.

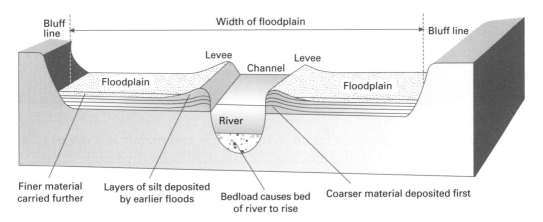

Figure 41 Floodplains and levees

Back swamps are parts of the floodplain that have become flooded and the flood water cannot drain back into the river.

Bluff line is a change in slope marking the point where the flood plain or river basin ends.

Examples of the above features of river deposition can be found in Ireland on the River Shannon and the Mulcair River, Limerick; and on the Mississippi River in the USA.

> **LQ** 1. Discuss the formation of any two Irish landforms you have studied with reference to the surface processes which formed them.

Choose any two of the following three features.

The first Irish landform I have studied is **waterfalls**. Examples of waterfalls found in Ireland include Torc Falls, Co. Kerry and

Powerscourt Falls, Co. Wicklow. International examples include Niagara Falls, Canada and Angel Falls, Venezuela.

Waterfalls are a feature of river erosion that are commonly found in the youthful stage of a river. They are formed as a result of vertical erosion of the river bed by the processes of hydraulic action, abrasion, attrition and solution.

Waterfalls can occur in a number of ways but are commonly formed when a band of hard rock lies across the river bed. As the river passes over the hard rock its erosive power increases. Because of this, the soft rock which is downstream from the hard rock is eroded very quickly, forming a small fall. As the water passes over the fall its speed increases. This in turn increases the rates of hydraulic action (the force of moving water) and abrasion (the river using its load to erode), which makes the fall steeper. Most erosion takes place at the base of the fall and a plunge pool forms here.

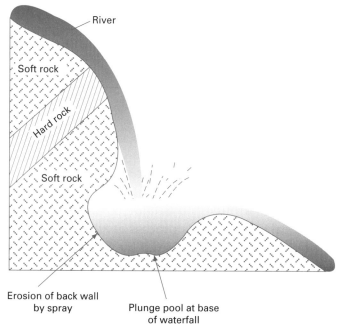

Figure 42 Waterfall

The back wall of the waterfall will be eroded by spray and in this way the fall may become undercut and eventually collapse. The collapsed rock will be broken down by attrition and will be moved downstream by a combination of solution, suspension, saltation and bottom traction.

Waterfalls can sometimes be found in the lower course as a result of river rejuvenation or tectonic activity.

The second feature I have studied is a **meander**. Such features are found in the mature stage of a river as it begins to slow down. Examples include the River Shannon near Roosky, Co. Roscommon and the River Boyne near Slane, Co. Meath.

A meander is a pronounced curve or bend found along the river's course. There are numerous processes involved in the formation of a meander including lateral erosion of the river banks by hydraulic action, abrasion, attrition and solution. The process of river deposition is also involved in the formation of meanders. River deposition occurs when a river slows down and drops its load.

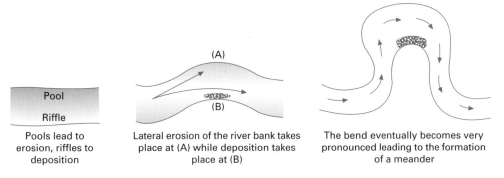

Pools lead to erosion, riffles to deposition

Lateral erosion of the river bank takes place at (A) while deposition takes place at (B)

The bend eventually becomes very pronounced leading to the formation of a meander

Figure 43 Formation of a meander

Along a straight stretch of river, pools and riffles develop. Pools are areas of deep water where erosion takes place. Riffles are areas of shallow water where deposition takes place. This process forms a slight bend.

As the river moves around the outside of the bend it erodes the bank by means of lateral erosion. This process is also known as bank caving and occurs where the bank is undercut by hydraulic action (the force of moving water). The undercut bank will eventually collapse and the material that is broken off will be transported downstream by processes such as suspension and saltation.

On the inside of the bend the river slows down and deposition takes place. This erosion and deposition causes the bend to become more pronounced thus forming a meander. As meanders become extremely pronounced they can form ox-bow lakes.

Another example of an Irish landform I have studied is a **delta**. Examples include the Nile Delta, the Mississippi Delta and the delta of the River Shannon. The processes involved in the formation of a delta include river transportation (solution, suspension, saltation and bottom traction) and deposition.

Deltas are a feature of river deposition. They form at the mouth of a river, where it enters the sea. When a river carrying a heavy load enters an area of calm water such as a sea or a lake, it slows down and deposition takes place. The material that is deposited will fall slowly to the sea floor and over time it will build up in layers called beds. There are three types of bed: bottom-set beds, fore-set beds and top-set beds. When these beds rise above sea level they form a fan-shaped island called a delta. Over time the delta will grow and extend out across the estuary dividing it into distributaries.

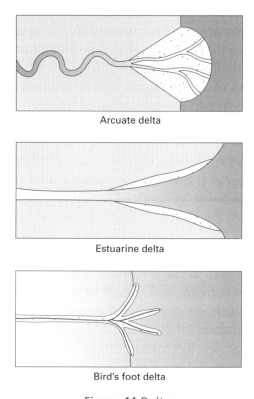

Arcuate delta

Estuarine delta

Bird's foot delta

Figure 44 Deltas

If deltas form at sea, they are called marine deltas. There are three types of marine delta: arcuate deltas, estuarine deltas and bird's foot deltas. There are numerous factors which influence the type of delta which forms, including the shape of the coastline and the nature of the river's load. If deltas form in a lake, they are called lacustrine deltas. Not all rivers form deltas. In most cases the river does not carry a sufficient load to form a delta and in other cases the ocean currents are too strong and simply move the sediment out to sea.

LQ 2. Discuss one way in which humans have interfered in surface processes.

An example of human interference in surface processes can be seen by the **construction of dams**. Dams such as the Aswan Dam on the River Nile in Egypt, the Three Gorges Dam on the Yangtze River in China and the numerous dams on the Colorado River in the USA provide evidence of this interference. Although dams have many economic benefits for humans, they greatly interfere with the natural fluvial processes of erosion, transportation and deposition.

In its simplest form a dam is a large wall built across a river in its upper course. Dams are most commonly found in the upper course of a river as rivers have most energy at this point and are carrying less sediment than in the lower course.

The construction of a dam across a river reduces the flow of water downstream and leads to the formation of a large lake or reservoir behind the dam. It is possible to regulate the size of this reservoir by regulating the flow of water through the dam. Water passes through the dam via large holes or penstocks at the base of the dam. As water flows through the penstocks it turns large wheels called turbines. These turbines are connected to generators which convert this kinetic energy into electricity.

This interference in river processes can have many positive effects for humans, the most obvious of which is the production of hydroelectric power. Another benefit is flood control: dams reduce the amount of water flowing downstream and therefore reduce the risk of flooding, which in turn protects residential and agricultural land. A third benefit is that the water contained in the artificial lake may be used as a domestic supply of water for nearby towns. Finally, the lake can also be used for recreational purposes.

Although human interference such as this can have positive effects, there are also many negative effects. These include loss of soil fertility, loss and damage to delta systems and flooding of land behind the dam. Good examples of the negative effects which human interference in surface processes can have include the Colorado River project and the Aral Sea project.

The Aral Sea is a major inland sea in Asia fed by the River Amu and the River Syr. The sea supported a large population in a number of ways. The variety of fish species in the sea supported a vibrant fishing sector. The rivers flooded regularly which provided fertile alluvium for thousands of hectares of land which supported the agricultural sector. Finally, where the rivers met the sea, a large delta with a diverse ecosystem had developed. In the mid-twentieth century the rivers were dammed in a number of places in order to irrigate millions of acres of unproductive land. Since the construction of the dams, the Aral Sea has shrunk to almost half its size, devastating the fishing sector. Also, the rivers no longer flood regularly and the previously fertile floodplains are now infertile. The delta has become a wasteland in a manner similar to the Colorado River delta, which suffered when numerous dams were built along its course.

---

3. **Discuss the effects which a drop in base level can have on the lower course of a river.**

LQ *Or*

Discuss the formation of features which form as a result of river rejuvenation.

Features which form as a result of river rejuvenation include knickpoints, terraces and incised meanders. **River rejuvenation** occurs when there is a drop in the base level of a river. The base level of a river is the lowest point to which a river can erode its bed and is the same as the level of the sea. Therefore a drop in base level means a drop in sea level. Changes in sea level are referred to as eustatic movement.

When sea level falls relative to the land, new land and new slope is added to the lower course of the river. The gradient of the river therefore becomes steeper and as a result the speed of the river increases. When the speed of the river increases the river starts to erode its bed again in a process known as vertical erosion, despite the fact that the river is in its old stage. Vertical erosion of a river bed usually only occurs in the youthful stage and when it occurs in the old stage the river is said to be rejuvenated. As the river erodes its bed, it may lead to the formation of rapids or even a waterfall. The point at which vertical erosion resumes is known as a **knickpoint**. Rivers can have several knickpoints, for example the River Shannon, reflecting the number of times sea levels have dropped.

A second feature formed as a result of river rejuvenation is a **terrace**. Rejuvenation involves vertical erosion of the river bed in its old stage. Rivers in their old stage tend to have a wide floodplain. When the river cuts down into its bed it often forms a waterfall. The river then continues on at a lower course. As the river continues on this lower course it erodes a new floodplain by means of lateral erosion. The old floodplain is now like a step above the new floodplain. This step is called a terrace. Steps found on both sides of a river are called paired terraces. If a river is rejuvenated a number of times, a number of terraces may occur. These are called stepped terraces.

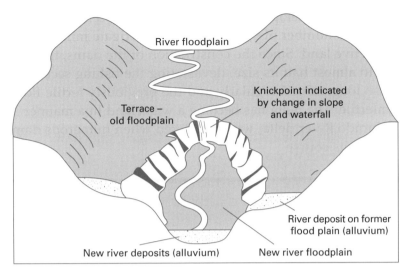

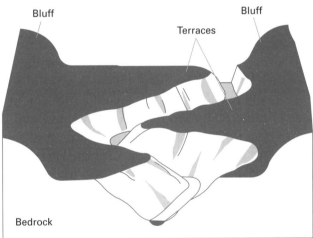

Figure 45 Features of river rejuvenation

Incised meanders also form as a result of river rejuvenation. In the old stage of a river the level of the river is quite high and almost level with the surrounding landscape. Rejuvenation, however, causes the river to erode its bed. When this occurs at meanders it leads to a seeming drop in the level of the river as it erodes downwards. This leaves relatively steep slopes at either side of the meander called incised meanders.

Topic **10**
Coasts

Waves influence all processes and landforms along the coast.
   There are two **types of wave**.

- **Destructive waves** are waves which remove part of the coastline and drag it back to sea. They occur on coastlines with a steep slope and lead to erosion.
- **Constructive waves** are waves which carry material back to the coastline and add to its mass. They occur on slopes with a gentle gradient and lead to deposition.

Processes of coastal erosion

- **Hydraulic action** is the force of waves as they crash against the coastline. It is most effective during storms when wave energy is strongest.
- **Abrasion** occurs when waves use their load (rocks and sand) to break down the coastline.
- **Attrition** is the process whereby rocks which have been eroded from the coastline and which are now part of a wave's load are broken down into smaller particles as they crash against each other within the wave.
- **Solution** occurs when the carbonic acid in the water allows it slowly to dissolve soluble rocks along the coast such as limestone and chalk.
- **Compressed air** occurs when a breaking wave traps or compresses air in the cracks and joints of rocks. As the wave retreats, the air expands rapidly and shatters the surrounding rock.

Process of coastal transportation

Longshore drift is the zigzag movement of material along the coastline and occurs when waves break at an angle to the beach. The incoming wave (swash) moves up the shore at an angle (obliquely) and either deposits or removes material. When this wave retreats (back wash) it moves straight back down the beach, not at an angle. The movement of waves in this zigzag manner results in the movement of material horizontally across the coastline.

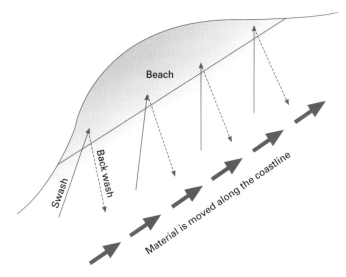

Figure 46 Longshore drift

Features of coastal erosion

For all coastal features you need to be able to: recognise the feature on a diagram or photograph, name and briefly explain the processes which led to its formation and give examples of the feature.

Cliffs and wave-cut platforms

Examples of cliffs and wave-cut platforms can be found at the Cliffs of Moher, Co. Clare; Ballybunion, Co. Kerry; and Killiney, Co. Dublin.

The processes involved in their formation are destructive waves, hydraulic action, abrasion, attrition, solution and compressed air.

Cliffs occur when destructive waves attack the base of the coastline at high tide level. Compressed air attacks lines of weakness in the rocks such as cracks and joints and widens them to form a notch. Over time the notch will increase in height, width and depth due to hydraulic action and abrasion.

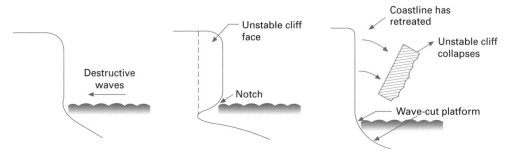

Figure 47 Cliffs and wave-cut platforms

This causes part of the cliff to become undercut. Eventually the undercut part of the cliff collapses and the coastline is said to have retreated.

Active coastlines are coastlines that are continually being eroded and are retreating. Inactive coastlines are coastlines where the wave-cut platform has prevented any further erosion from taking place.

Sea caves, arches, stacks, stumps, blow holes and geos

Examples of these features can be found at Kilkee, Co. Clare; Skellig Rocks, Co. Kerry; and the Twelve Apostles, Australia.

The processes involved in their formation are destructive waves, hydraulic action, abrasion, attrition, solution and compressed air.

Sea caves occur when destructive waves attack the base of a headland and compressed air erodes a notch along a line of weakness. This notch will increase in size as a result of hydraulic action and abrasion and over time forms a sea cave.

Blow holes occur as a result of erosion in the roof of a cave. It is a chimney-like tunnel in the cave roof formed when spray from waves hitting the back of the cave shoots upwards.

A **geo** may develop if the part of the coastline between a blow hole and the front of the cliff collapses.

Sea arches occur if the back of a sea cave is eroded sufficiently so that it penetrates the other side of the headland.

Sea stacks form when the roof of a sea cave or a sea arch collapses.

Sea stumps form when a sea stack is broken down by the processes of coastal erosion and weathering.

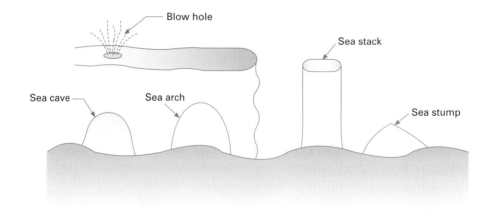

Figure 48 Sea caves, arches, stacks, stumps and blow holes

Bays and headlands

Examples of bays and headlands include Old Head of Kinsale, Co. Cork; Teelin, Co. Donegal; Galway Bay; and Clew Bay.

The processes involved in their formation are differential erosion (this occurs when different parts of the coast are eroded at different rates), abrasion, attrition, solution, compressed air and hydraulic action.

Bays and headlands form when a coastline is composed of alternate areas of hard and soft rock. Destructive waves will erode the soft rock at a faster rate than the hard rock, thus forming inlets and bays. The resistant outcrops of hard rock which remain are known as headlands. Eventually, as the coastline matures and the bays become sheltered, the headlands become the focus of most erosion. As a result of this, features such as sea caves and sea arches form at their base.

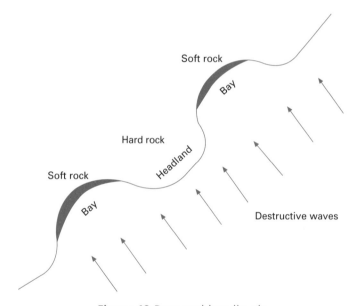

Figure 49 Bays and headlands

Features of coastal deposition

Beaches

Examples of beaches include Lahinch, Co. Clare; Ballybunion, Co. Kerry; and Coogee Beach, Sydney, Australia.

The processes involved in their formation are constructive waves and longshore drift.

A beach is defined as all material that is found between the areas of low tide and high tide. The material found on a beach is material that has been eroded elsewhere, broken down by attrition and transported by longshore drift before being deposited on the beach by constructive waves.

The upper beach or backshore has a steep slope and contains material such as rocks, pebbles, boulders and shingle. The lower beach or foreshore has a gentle slope and contains sand and shingle.

Storm beaches occur when storm waves carry rocks and boulders above the high tide mark. Most of Ireland's storm beaches are man-made in order to guard against erosion.

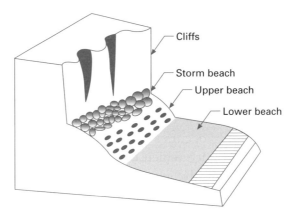

Figure 50 Beaches

Sand spits, tombolos and off-shore bars

Examples of these features can be found at Inch Strand, Dingle, Co. Kerry; and at Cape Cod, Massachusetts, USA.

The processes involved in their formation are constructive waves and longshore drift.

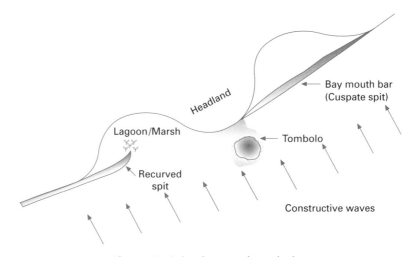

Figure 51 Spits, bars and tombolos

A **sand spit** is a feature of coastal deposition which has one end connected to land and another pointing out to sea or across a bay or estuary. Sand spits form in areas where there is a dramatic change in coastal direction such as the entry to a bay or estuary.

There are three types of spit: recurved spits, cuspate spits (bay mouth bar) and double spits. Slower waves behind the spit often result in the formation of a lagoon or salt marsh in this area.

When an island is connected to the mainland by a spit it is known as a **tombolo**.

LQ **1. Discuss the features formed on the Irish landscape as a result of isostatic processes.**

An example of a feature formed on the Irish landscape as a result of isostatic processes is a **raised beach** or a **raised cliff**. Isostatic movement refers to a change in the level of the land, usually a rise in the level of the land. This commonly occurs at the end of an ice age when the pressure of the overlying ice which had laid upon the land for thousands of years is released. When the ice melts and the pressure is released the

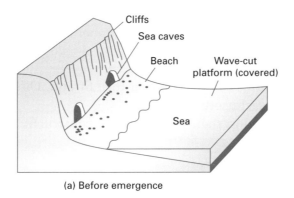

(a) Before emergence

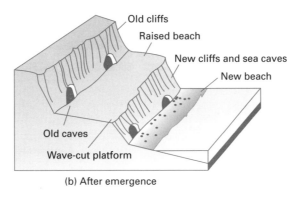

(b) After emergence

Figure 52 Formation of raised beaches and cliffs

land steadily rises in response. This movement can last thousands of years. The last ice age in Europe (the Pleistocene) ended 30,000 years ago and yet parts of Ireland are still rising. This process is best observed in coastal areas.

As the land along the coast rises, features such as cliffs, caves and beaches are no longer directly exposed to the sea. New land is now exposed and therefore new cliffs and beaches form. The older features are now called raised cliffs and raised beaches. Examples of these features can be seen at Blackhead Beach, Co. Clare. The areas where such features are found are known as coastlines of emergence.

A second feature that is produced by isostatic movement is a river **knickpoint**. When the level of the land rises at the end of an ice age, new land and new slope is added to the lower course of a river. The gradient of the river is now steeper and the speed of the river increases.

When the speed of the river increases the river starts to erode its bed again in a process known as vertical erosion, despite the fact that the river is in its old stage. Vertical erosion of a river bed usually only occurs in the youthful stage and when it occurs in the old stage the river is said to be rejuvenated. As the river erodes its bed, it may lead to the formation of rapids or even a waterfall. The point at which vertical erosion resumes is known as a knickpoint. Some rivers can have several knickpoints. Examples of these knickpoints can be seen on the River Shannon.

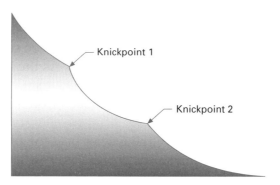

Figure 53 River knickpoints

Topic **11**
Glaciation

Types of glacier

- **Continental ice sheets** are large accumulations of ice that cover large portions of a land mass or continent, for example Greenland or the Antarctic. Ireland was covered by an ice sheet during the last ice age (Pleistocene).
- **Valley glaciers** are sometimes called alpine glaciers and are usually confined to mountain valleys.

Causes of ice ages

Milankovitch argued that when the following three changes coincide they may lead to an ice age:

- Orbital stretch – every 100,000 years
- Tilting of the earth's axis – every 40,000 years
- Wobble of the earth – every 23,000 years.

Processes of glacial erosion

- **Plucking** occurs when meltwater, created by friction, seeps into the cracks and joints of the rocks which the glacier meets. As the glacier moves over the rock, the meltwater freezes, causing the rock to stick to the glacier. When the glacier moves on, the rock is plucked from the landscape and becomes part of the glacier's load.
- **Abrasion** is the process whereby the glacier uses the plucked rocks (its load) to scrape, scour and polish the surface over which it moves. This leaves deep grooves or scratches on the landscape called striations or glacial striae.

Processes of glacial transportation

- **Pressure melting** occurs due to friction from obstructions on the valley floor and sides. The glacier melts and shrinks in order to bypass the obstruction.

- **Basal sliding** occurs when friction between the base of the glacier and the valley floor causes small streams to form below the glacier. The glacier then slides down slope on these streams.
- **Laminar flow** – glaciers form in layers. Fault lines can develop between layers and some layers can move down slope faster than others.

Features of glacial erosion

For all glacial features you need to be able to: recognise the feature on a diagram or photograph, name and briefly explain the processes which led to its formation and give examples of the feature.

Corries

Examples of corries include the Devil's Punch Bowl, Macgillycuddy's Reeks, Co. Kerry; and Coomshingaun, Comeragh Mountains, Co. Waterford.

The processes involved in their formation are plucking and abrasion.

A corrie or cirque is a basin-shaped hollow, cut into the side of a mountain. Corries are formed when snow accumulates in a small hollow above the snow line which was formed by weathering. The overlying layers of snow will compress, percolate and crystallise the lower layers, forming blue glacial ice. Eventually the ice becomes too big for the hollow and moves down slope, pulling a large portion of the back wall with it. This leaves a large gap in the back wall called a bergschrund.

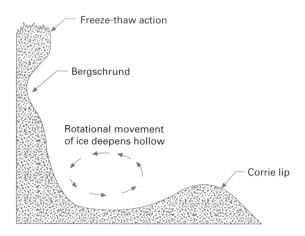

Figure 54 Corrie

U-shaped valleys

Examples of U-shaped valleys include Glendalough, Co. Wicklow; and the Gap of Dunloe, Macgillycuddy's Reeks, Co. Kerry.

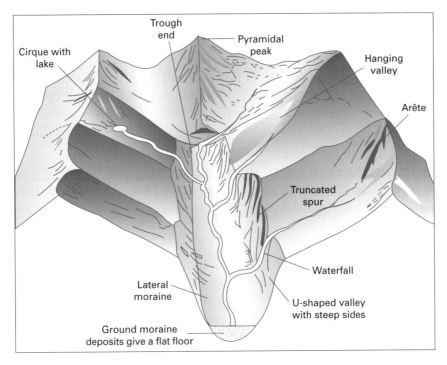

Figure 55 U-shaped valley

The processes involved in their formation are plucking and abrasion.

U-shaped valleys occur when a glacier leaves a corrie and advances down slope through pre-existing river valleys. As the glacier advances, it changes the profile of the valley from V-shaped to U-shaped by means of plucking and abrasion.

A **pyramidal peak** is the steep-sided peak of a mountain which has been subjected to glacial erosion. An example is the Matterhorn, Switzerland.

A **truncated spur** occurs when the ends of interlocking spurs that had projected into the V-shaped valley are eroded or cut off by the processes of glacial erosion. An example is Cumeenduff Glen, Killarney, Co. Kerry.

Hanging valleys occur when a tributary glacier joins a main glacier. After glaciation, when rivers return to these valleys, waterfalls may be found here. An example is the Doo Lough Valley, Co. Mayo.

Ribbon lakes or pater noster lakes form when a glacier encounters patches of hard and soft rock on the valley floor as it advances down valley. The soft rock is eroded easily by plucking and abrasion to form deep grooves on the valley floor. After glaciation, these grooves will fill in with water to form lakes. An example of a ribbon lake can be found at the Gap of Dunloe, Killarney, Co. Kerry.

Glacial deposition

When a glacier reaches the lowlands it is carrying a heavy load. In the lowlands the glacier will start to slow down, lose its competence and begin to deposit its load on the landscape. Glaciers deposit two types of material.

- **Boulder clay deposition** is material that was deposited **directly** by the glacier. It is unsorted, unstratified and produces a fertile soil.
- **Fluvial-glacial deposition** occurs when meltwater streams flow away from the ice sheet as it melts. These streams carry parts of the glacier's load with them. Eventually the streams slow down and deposit this material far away from the glacier. This material is sorted, stratified and relatively infertile.

Feature of boulder clay deposition: Moraines

Examples of moraines can be found in Ovens, Co. Cork and in Jutland, Denmark.

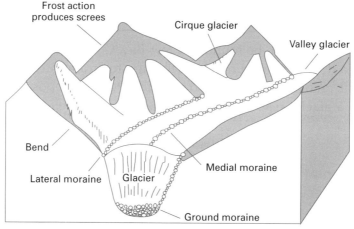

Valley Glacier

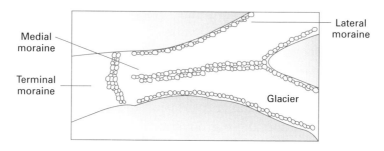

Figure 56 Moraine

Lateral moraines are ridges of boulder clay found along either side of the lower part of a glacial valley. They represent material which the glacier had eroded in the uplands and carried along its sides before depositing it in the lowlands as it started to melt and retreat.

Medial moraines are ridges of boulder clay which run along the centre of the lower valley. They were formed when a tributary glacier joined a main glacier forming a single large glacier. The lateral moraines of the two single glaciers joined and formed a ridge of material running though the middle of the newly enlarged glacier. This material was deposited when the glacier reached the lowlands and began to melt as it retreated.

Terminal moraines are ridges of boulder clay which run horizontally across the valley. They represent material which the glacier pushed in front of itself in a bulldozing fashion as it advanced down valley. A terminal moraine marks the furthest point which the ice advanced to and is usually crescent shaped.

Englacial moraines comprise material which was carried inside the glacier and was later deposited as the glacier retreated.

Ground moraines comprise material which was transported beneath the glacier and was later deposited as the glacier retreated.

Feature of boulder clay deposition: Drumlins

Examples of drumlins can be found at Clew Bay, Co. Mayo; Drumline, Co. Clare; and in a drumlin belt running from Sligo to Strangford Lough.

A drumlin is an oval or egg-shaped mound of glacial deposition which was formed when a glacier reached the lowlands, began to melt and retreat, lost

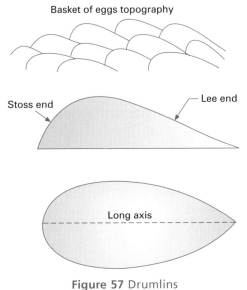

Figure 57 Drumlins

its competence (its ability to carry its load) and deposited large mounds of boulder clay. Drumlins usually occur in groups or clusters in what is known as a 'basket of eggs topography'.

Drumlins have a steep side called the stoss end and a less steep side called the lee end. The stoss end faces the direction from which the ice advanced. The long axis of a drumlin lies in the direction of ice movement.

Feature of fluvial-glacial deposition: Eskers

Examples of eskers include the Esker Riada which runs between Dublin and Galway; and Clonmacnoise, Co. Offaly.

An esker is a winding ridge of fluvial-glacial material that represents deposition which took place on the beds of streams which flowed beneath the ice sheet. Eskers have many uses. They are often the foundation for route ways in poorly drained areas and are often quarried by the construction sector as they contain sands and gravels.

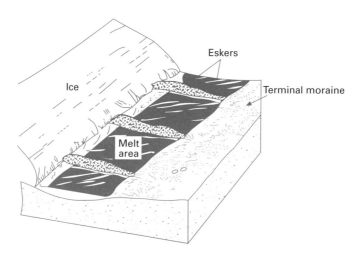

Figure 58 Eskers

Feature of fluvial-glacial deposition: Outwash plains

Examples of outwash plains include The Curragh, Co. Kildare and Western Jutland, Denmark.

An outwash plain is a flat area of land where meltwater streams, which flowed from the ice sheet as it melted, deposited material such as sands and gravels. Outwash plains generally contain infertile soils.

Feature of fluvial-glacial deposition: Kames and kettle holes

Kettle holes are depressions found on an outwash plain. They were formed when blocks of ice were buried with glacial deposits. When these blocks of

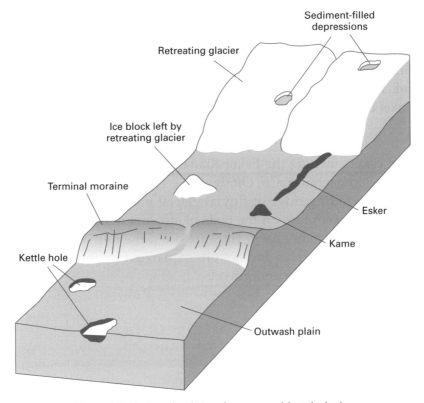

Figure 59 Outwash plains, kames and kettle holes

ice eventually melted, the overlying land slumped to form a depression called a kettle hole.

Kames are small mounds of deposition found on an outwash plain. They form as a result of different meltwater streams carrying different amounts of material.

Section **2**
Regional Geography

Questions on regional geography in the Leaving Certificate consist of shorter questions worth eight marks each, and longer questions worth twenty or thirty marks each. The longer questions appear in the text with an 'LQ' before them.

The topics covered in this section are:

Topic **12**
The Concept of a Region

Climatic regions

Climatic regions are areas of the earth's surface that share similar levels of temperature and precipitation. Areas of land can be thousands of kilometres apart and still be part of the same climatic region. Europe contains at least five climatic regions.

A **cool temperate maritime climate** is found in Ireland and throughout north-western Europe. It generally has mild winters and warm summers.

A **Mediterranean climate** is a two-season climate found in areas such as southern Spain, southern Italy, southern France and Greece.

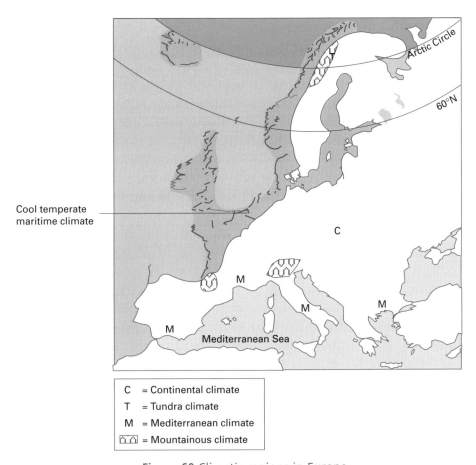

Figure 60 Climatic regions in Europe

A **continental climate** experiences extremes of temperature and can be found in the interior of continents, away from the heating effects of warm ocean currents. This climate is found in, for example, parts of Germany and northern Switzerland.

A **tundra climate** is found in the high latitudes of the northern hemisphere. Examples of countries which are part of this climatic region include northern Scandinavia and northern Russia.

A **mountainous climate** has temperatures which can vary above and below 0°C. Examples include the Pyrenees and the Alps.

LQ 1. Discuss the characteristics of any one climatic region you have studied.

The climatic region I have studied is the **cool temperate maritime climate**. This is also known as the cool temperate oceanic climate. This climate is commonly found between 40° and 69° north of the equator. The countries that experience this climate are generally countries in north-western Europe which border the Atlantic Ocean. Examples include Ireland, Britain, western Scandinavia, Denmark, Belgium, north-west France and north-west Spain.

The cool temperate maritime climate tends to have cool summers and mild winters. Countries which experience this climate also tend to have a smaller temperature range than those which experience a continental climate. In most cases annual temperature range is rarely more than 10°C. This is due to the influence of nearby ocean currents. In the case of western Europe it is the North Atlantic Drift that is the dominant influence on climate. Although water takes time to heat up during the summer it retains this heat long into winter giving countries such as Ireland winter temperatures as mild as 4°C and summers averaging 16°C.

The cool temperate maritime climate tends to have high levels of precipitation as the moisture source is nearby. The prevailing winds are south-westerly. These winds bring in depressions which have gathered moisture as they blew over the Atlantic Ocean. As the winds reach the coast they rise, and as they rise so they cool, leading to regular levels of precipitation throughout the year. In Ireland most precipitation falls in the west of the country given the presence of mountain ranges such as the Nephin Beg Mountains and Maumturk Mountains. The east of the country lies in a rain shadow and as such receives less precipitation.

Geomorphologic/physical regions

Geomorphologic or physical regions are regions which were formed as a result of endogenic forces (forces that create landforms) such as plate tectonics. Such regions include mountains, valleys and volcanic islands.

Examples of geomorphologic regions are the Burren, Co. Clare; the Munster ridge and valley province; and the North European Plain.

The **Munster ridge and valley province** was formed during the American fold movement 250 million years ago. This occurred when the African plate moved north and collided with the Eurasian plate causing the crust in Munster to buckle and wrinkle. The surface layers of Carboniferous limestone and the underlying old red sandstone were folded into ridges and valleys that ran from east to west. Many of the limestone valleys are now home to rivers such as the Blackwater and the Lee.

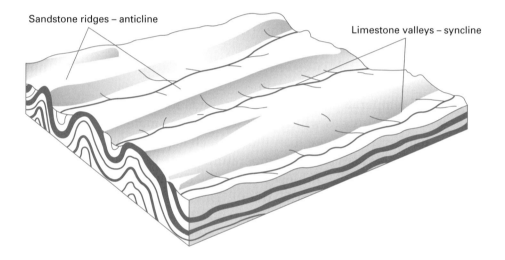

Figure 61 The Munster ridge and valley province

The **North European Plain** is a lowland region that covers Ireland, Britain, southern Sweden and Finland, Belgium, Holland, northern Germany, Poland, Lithuania and Latvia.

Fifty million years ago Ireland and Britain were connected to mainland Europe (as the North Sea did not form until the end of the last ice age) and the newly formed Alpine and American fold mountains were being subjected to intense weathering and erosion, in the process producing millions of tons of sediment. A combination of wind, water and ice transported this material onto the area of land occupied by the present-day countries mentioned above. As this material was deposited it levelled the land forming the North European Plain.

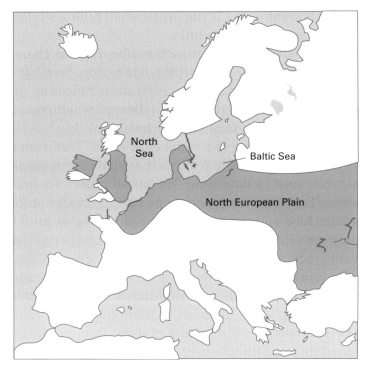

Figure 62 The North European Plain

2. Discuss the characteristics of any one physical or geomorphologic region you have studied.

The geomorphologic region I have studied is the **Burren, Co. Clare**. It is obvious that the Burren is a distinctive geomorphologic region as it contains numerous landforms such as limestone pavements and swallow holes.

Limestone pavements are a distinctive feature found in karst regions, which form as a result of the process of chemical weathering known as carbonation. Limestone pavements form when overlying layers of soil and vegetation are removed, usually by glacial erosion. Once the protective overgrowth is removed the limestone is exposed at the surface. Limestone consists of vertical joints and horizontal bedding planes. Where the joints reach the surface they represent lines of weakness and are the first part of the rock to be attacked by carbonation.

Carbonation results in small gashes forming in the rock. These gashes will gather rainfall which increases the amount of carbonation taking place. This in turn deepens the gashes which are now termed grikes. The flat slabs of limestone that separate grikes are called clints. A combination of clints and grikes is known as a limestone pavement. The clints are also weathered by carbonation, albeit at a much slower rate.

Evidence of this weathering is the many small hollows called karrens which can be observed on the clints.

Swallow holes are another feature that illustrate the characteristics of the Burren as a distinctive geomorphologic region. Swallow holes or sink holes are also referred to as sluggas. A swallow hole is an opening in the bed of a river which allows the river to disappear underground where it then continues on its course at a lower level.

Swallow holes can occur in a number of ways. They commonly form when an area of impermeable rock such as shale meets an area of permeable rock such as limestone. The initial cause of a swallow hole is groundwater. This is water which seeps into the cracks or joints of the pervious limestone and continues to seep downwards until it reaches a layer of impermeable rock. Because the water cannot pass through the impermeable rock, it accumulates above it and saturates the overlying rock. This saturated rock is eventually dissolved by the carbonic acid in the water, thus forming hundreds of kilometres of underground tunnels. Swallow holes form when the roofs of these tunnels collapse and a river that had been flowing on the surface plunges through the hole and flows underground through the pre-existing tunnels. As the river flows through the tunnels, it may enlarge them in places to form caves or caverns. Swallow holes usually have the shape of an inverted cone.

Administrative regions

Administrative regions are regions which are defined by the type and manner of their administration. Administrative regions can be local (Clare County Council), devolved (Wales), national (Ireland) or supranational (EU).

Examples of administrative regions include the local authority areas in Ireland; French departments; and the European Union (EU).

> **LQ** **3.** **Discuss the characteristics of any one administrative region you have studied.**

Ireland's local authority areas are a good example of administrative regions. Local government in Ireland is covered by the Local Government Act 2001, which established a two-tier structure.

The top tier of the structure consists of twenty-nine county councils and five city councils. Twenty-four of the twenty-six traditional counties have had county councils since 1898. Tipperary has had two, one for North Tipperary and one for South Tipperary. Since 1994 County Dublin has had three councils: Dún Laoghaire–Rathdown, Fingal and South Dublin. The five cities of Dublin, Cork, Limerick, Galway and Waterford have city councils, which have the same status as county councils.

The second tier of local government consists of town or borough councils. There are eighty such councils. Outside the towns the county councils are solely responsible for the provision of services.

Local councils' funding comes from a variety of sources. Much revenue was derived from water and refuse charges, however these proved extremely unpopular and water charges, were abolished in 1997. The Irish exchequer is a significant source of funding at present and additional sources of income include service charges, housing rents and borrowing. The money gathered by local authorities is used to provide a number of services for the local community.

Local government is responsible for matters such as planning, local roads, sanitation and libraries. Local authorities are also required to draw up county development plans, which set out the development of both rural and urban areas for the next five years. In recent years the responsibilities of local authorities have dwindled, as highlighted by the replacement of the regional health boards with the central Health Service Executive (HSE).

Cultural regions

Cultural regions are defined by language or religion. This may be evident in the constructed landscape, i.e. place names or architecture.

Examples of cultural regions include Belgium and the Gaeltacht regions in Ireland.

> **LQ** **4. Discuss the causes and consequences of cultural division in a European region you have studied.**

The European region I have studied is **Belgium**. In Belgium, language and culture have led to a divide between the Flemish population in Flanders in the north of the country and the Walloon population in the south of the country.

The Flemish are of Germanic descent and speak Flemish, which is a dialect of Dutch. They are strongly Catholic and conservative in outlook. Until the mid to late twentieth century they were a minority of the Belgian population and were regarded as socially inferior by their neighbours in the south. In this period Flanders was a predominantly rural economy and was industrially underdeveloped. Today the Flemish are a majority (60 per cent) of the Belgian population with high birth rates and Flanders is the industrial core of Belgium. The discovery of oil and gas in the North Sea in the 1960s greatly assisted the economic development of the region.

The Walloon population in the south of Belgium are of Celtic origin and speak French. In the past they made up a majority of the Belgian population and were the cultural elite. This coincided with a period when the south was Belgium's industrial core, due to large deposits of coal at Borinage, Liège and Charleroi. However as the coal declined, both in terms of quantity and in terms of its use in modern industry, so too did the region of Wallonia. Unemployment levels soared. Today the Walloons are a minority of the population and out-migration from the south to the north is a major problem.

The cultural divide in Belgium between north and south has often been reflected politically. In the 1960s the Flemish population resisted attempts by the predominantly Walloon government to have French declared as the official language of the state. Today both languages enjoy that status. The clear divisions between the cultural groups were finally recognised in the 1990s when three administrative regions were set up in Belgium. Each region is now responsible for the development of educational, social and cultural matters.

Cultural conflict is still evident however, particularly around Brussels where the French-speaking city is expanding into the Flemish-speaking countryside as a result of in-migration from the south.

Core and peripheral regions

Core regions are regions which have favourable physical and economic characteristics. They generally have a physical environment which favours productive agriculture. They enjoy a favourable climate, low-lying relief and fertile soils. Core regions usually have high populations and high population densities as a result of in-migration from surrounding areas. In core regions one generally finds a productive primary sector with a well-developed secondary sector. Core regions usually display modern, well-developed transport infrastructures and have a wide range of high, medium and low order services. Jobs are available in all sectors.

Examples of core regions include the Greater Dublin Area, the North Italian Plain and the Paris Basin.

Peripheral regions are regions which display unfavourable physical and economic characteristics. Peripheral regions in Europe are not poor; they are merely underdeveloped compared to core regions. The physical environment in peripheral regions is unsuited to productive agriculture. They have a harsh climate (either too hot or too cold), mountainous relief and infertile soils. They usually have low populations and low population densities as a result of out-migration. In peripheral regions there is an overdependence on an underdeveloped primary sector, with a lack of available jobs in the secondary sector. Peripheral regions usually have an underdeveloped transport infrastructure and a lack of high order services such as hospitals and colleges.

Examples of peripheral regions include the West of Ireland, the Mezzogiorno in Italy and northern Scandinavia.

A = Greater Dublin Area (core region)
B = Central Lakes Lowlands of Sweden (core region)
C = North Italian Plain (core region)
D = Paris Basin (core region)
E = West of Ireland (peripheral region)
F = Northern Scandinavia (peripheral region)
G = Mezzogiorno (peripheral region)

Figure 63 Core and peripheral regions in Europe

Old industrial regions in decline; economically depressed regions; a core region experiencing problems

Each of the above terms refers to the same type of region, for example the Sambre-Meuse Valley in Belgium or Bilbao in Spain.

LQ **5.** Core regions may fall into economic decline. Explain why this decline may occur with reference to a region you have studied.

The region I have studied is the **Sambre-Meuse Valley** in Belgium. This region was Belgium's core economic region in the 1800s and 1900s. The coalfields at Borinage, Liège and Charleroi provided large-scale employment, both direct and indirect. Direct employment took the form of mining and extraction of coal. The coal also provided indirect employment in the form of the many factories which located in this region to avail of coal as a raw material. In this period coal was the dominant power source for industry. However by the mid to late twentieth century this region had become economically depressed and the last of Belgium's coal mines was closed in the 1980s by the European Coal and Steel Community (ECSC).

There are a number of reasons for the decline of the Sambre-Meuse Valley. The intensive mining of coal for over two hundred years, particularly during the two world wars, meant that by the 1960s the best seams of coal were exhausted. Also, as the twentieth century progressed, coal declined in importance as a raw material for industry. This period saw the emergence of new industries such as electrometallurgical and petrochemical industries. These industries do not require coal as a raw material and as such had no incentive to locate in the Sambre-Meuse region. They instead located in more attractive coastal locations in Flanders, which was rapidly becoming a popular destination for industry as a result of its access to the North Sea.

The decline of the Sambre-Meuse Valley has had many consequences for the region. High unemployment levels led to large-scale out-migration, particularly of the younger workforce, to the now prosperous Flanders. This out-migration led to lower birth rates and the eventual closure of services, such as schools, in the worst affected areas. It proved difficult to attract modern industry as the infrastructure of the region was completely outdated and unsuited to the demands of new industries. The workforce that remained in the region was largely elderly and unskilled. Furthermore, the physical environment of the region was not attractive due to the prevalence of abandoned mining towns and slag heaps.

There are numerous solutions to the problems faced by the Sambre-Meuse Valley, some of which have already been adopted. Infrastructure has been improved with the construction of the Albert Canal, which links the region to the North Sea. Grants, loans and subsidies have been used to attract modern communications companies to cities such as Liège and this process must continue if the region is to prosper once more. Education and retraining of the workforce is also necessary to attract industry.

Topic **13**
The West of Ireland: A Peripheral Region in Ireland

LQ

1. Draw a sketch map of an Irish region you have studied and on it mark and name the following:

   (a) The relief of the region
   (b) The drainage of the region
   (c) An agricultural area
   (d) An industrial area
   (e) An urban centre.

The region I have studied is the **West of Ireland**.

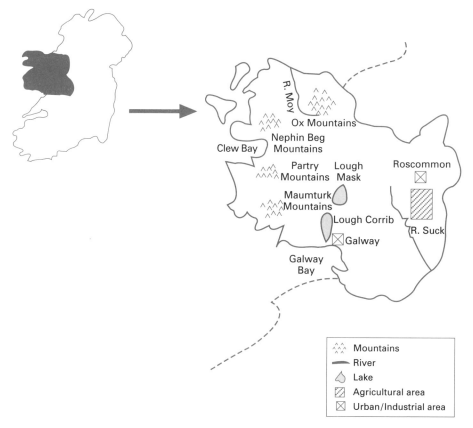

Figure 64 The West of Ireland – Ireland's peripheral region

LQ 2. Discuss the physical processes present in any one Irish region you have studied.

The region I have studied is the **West of Ireland**. The **relief** of the West of Ireland consists of both mountains and lowland plains. Much of the west coast was submerged by the sea at the end of the last ice age (Pleistocene) and as a result has many bays and inlets. Also in the western part of the region one finds numerous mountains which have been heavily glacially eroded. The dominant mountain ranges are the Nephin Beg Mountains, the Partry Mountains and the Maumturk Mountains. These were formed during the Caledonian fold movement 400 million years ago when the American plate collided with the Eurasian plate. Low-lying land can be found in the east of the region in Co. Roscommon. Most of the region has either granite or metamorphic rocks at the surface. These rocks produce infertile soils when weathered.

The **climate** in the region is cool temperate maritime and it is relatively mild throughout the winter months with January temperatures of about 4°C. The North Atlantic Drift has a moderating influence that keeps winter temperatures mild. The climate is wet and precipitation averages 1,600 mm per year. Prevailing winds are south-westerly. These winds draw up large amounts of moisture as they move over the Atlantic Ocean. When the winds then reach the coastline they rise to move over the mountainous areas. As they rise they cool and condense leading to large amounts of relief rain throughout the year.

The **soils** in this region are generally infertile and bad for agriculture. The underlying granite produces a poor clay soil when it is weathered. In mountainous areas there are numerous peat soils with a low mineral content that are only suited to forestry. Also, in areas where some fertile soils are found, leaching has brought many of the minerals to the lower horizons and in some cases has led to the formation of podzols. Some pockets of brown-earths are found in parts of Co. Galway.

The dominant rivers **draining** the region are the River Moy, the River Suck and the River Corrib. Many of these rivers flow in the synclines created by the Caledonian fold movement. Tributaries include the River Boyle and the River Fergus. The main lakes in the region are Lough Corrib, Lough Mask and Lough Conn.

LQ 3. Discuss the development of primary activities in any one Irish region you have studied.

The region I have studied is the **West of Ireland**. The dominant primary activities in this region are **agriculture** and **fishing**.

Agriculture in the West of Ireland is generally unproductive and subsistent. This is due to a number of factors such as the moist climate, infertile soils, mountainous relief and distance from markets.

The prevalence of bog land, the windy and wet weather and the mountainous relief mean that pastoral farming is dominant with little arable farming. Sixty-six per cent of farmers in the west are drystock farmers which does not provide a large income. Farm sizes are smaller than in the east, with the average size being only 21 hectares.

Many farms in the West of Ireland are run by older farmers, who tend to be conservative and reluctant to change from traditional practices. Fifty-two per cent of farmers in the region are over 55 years of age.

The West of Ireland has fewer large urban centres to act as markets for food products. Therefore, farmers face added transport costs not only because they are isolated from the European market but also the main Irish market (the Dublin region). All of these factors have combined to make agriculture in the west unproductive and yet it is still one of the region's biggest employers.

The second primary activity found in the West of Ireland is fishing. Despite the peripheral nature of this region, the fishing sector is well developed in comparison to the core Dublin area. This is mainly due to favourable factors in the physical environment. The West of Ireland has an extensive coastline on the Atlantic Ocean and has a considerable continental shelf. The continental shelf contains shallow waters which allow the growth of plankton which in turn attracts many species of fish such as mackerel, herring, cod and whiting.

Fishing plays an important role in the economy of the region. Although direct employment in the fishing sector is quite small, indirect employment in areas such as fish processing and aquaculture means that more than 2,500 people depend on the fishing sector in this region. This figure would have been much higher in the past but the number of fishermen has declined in recent years due to a number of factors.

Because of the Common Fisheries Policy (CFP) and the introduction of quotas by the European Union there is little room for expansion in the region's fishing sector, however additional employment can be generated in the development of aquaculture. Aquaculture is the artificial breeding of fish. Aquaculture is most extensively practised in Clew Bay and over 200 people are employed in this sector.

---

4. Discuss the extent to which the physical processes in an Irish region you have studied have limited the development of agriculture in that region.

LQ

The region I have studied is the **West of Ireland**. It is obvious that the physical characteristics of this region, such as climate, relief and soils, have negatively affected the development of the agricultural sector. Agriculture in the West of Ireland is generally unproductive and subsistent. This is due to a number of factors such as the moist climate, infertile soils and mountainous relief.

The maritime climate in the region, although ensuring mild winters which benefit agriculture, also provides consistent precipitation which can lead to leaching of soils. The mountainous relief, particularly in the west of the region, also affects agriculture. The Nephin Beg Mountains, Maumturk Mountains and Partry Mountains all make mechanisation of agriculture difficult and render this part of the region completely unsuitable for arable farming.

The soils in this region are generally infertile and bad for agriculture. The underlying granite produces a poor clay soil when it is weathered. In mountainous areas there are numerous peat soils with a low mineral content that are only suited to forestry. Also, in areas where some fertile soils are found, leaching has brought many of the minerals to the lower horizons and in some cases has led to the formation of podzols which make productive agriculture difficult.

The prevalence of bog land, the windy and wet weather and the mountainous relief mean that pastoral farming is dominant with little arable farming. Sixty-six per cent of farmers in the west are involved in drystock farming, which does not provide a large income. Also, many farms in the west are run by older farmers (52 per cent of farmers are over 55 years of age) who tend to be conservative and reluctant to change from traditional practices. Furthermore, the west has fewer large urban centres to act as markets for food products and therefore farmers face added transport costs because they are isolated not only from the European market but also from the main Irish market in the Dublin region. In the West of Ireland, farm sizes are smaller than in the east with the average size being only 21 hectares.

Although there are numerous reasons why the agricultural sector in the West is unproductive, it seems certain that the unfavourable physical landscape is the main reason.

LQ 5. Discuss the factors which have limited the development of manufacturing in an Irish region you studied.

The region I have studied is the **West of Ireland**. The manufacturing sector in the peripheral West of Ireland is much less developed than in the core Dublin region.

There are a number of reasons why the west has struggled to attract large multinational companies to the region. The west has a relatively unskilled workforce in comparison to the Dublin region. The National University of Ireland, Galway is the only university in the region, whereas Dublin has three major universities producing large amounts of graduates in growth industries such as the IT sector.

Distance from markets also hinders the development of a manufacturing sector. The west is not only isolated from Ireland's main market, which is the Dublin region, but the lack of a deep-water port also isolates the region from the lucrative European Union market. This distance from markets increases transport costs for industries locating in the west.

The weak primary sector in the west also affects the manufacturing sector as there are no large-scale spin-offs from agriculture in the form of food processing and agricultural machinery. The poor infrastructure of the west in the form of airports, ports and motorways has also discouraged inward investment.

There have been numerous attempts to develop a productive manufacturing sector in the west. The Celtic Tiger economy of the 1990s helped attract multinational companies to the region. The Western Development Commission was set up in order to ensure that all counties in the West of Ireland benefited from this and that not all manufacturing was centred on Galway City with other areas simply becoming commuter towns.

Also, the National Development Plan stresses the need to upgrade road, rail and air access to the region in order to reduce the isolated nature of the region from major markets. The importance of providing modern infrastructure to attract investment is highlighted by the need to roll out broadband telecommunications throughout the region.

The traditional industries of textiles, food processing and clothing are gradually being replaced by more modern industries such as healthcare, electronics and biotechnology. These are highly skilled industries and will require continued investment in third-level education in the region.

Despite the prosperity enjoyed in recent decades, and the re-opening of part of the western rail corridor, the infrastructure of the west remains severely underdeveloped.

LQ 6. Discuss the development of tertiary activities in any one Irish region you have studied.

The region I have studied is the **West of Ireland**. The tertiary activities I have chosen to discuss are **tourism** and **transport**. As is common in peripheral regions, both of these sectors are underdeveloped.

The tourist sector in the west is seen as the best way of stimulating the economy of the region as it is a labour-intensive sector. The west is very attractive to tourists for a number of reasons. The River Shannon, with its lakes and boating facilities, borders Counties Galway and Roscommon. The River Moy also has good fishing facilities. The coastal scenery, including Killary Harbour, Achill Island and Clew Bay, is among the most spectacular in the world. Most of all, the cultural attractions in the west help develop the tourist sector. Counties Mayo and Galway have Gaeltacht regions and there are hundreds of historical attractions throughout the west.

The tourist sector generated €500 million for the region in 1999 but remains underdeveloped. Also, Galway accounts for the majority of this income. Any strategy to develop tourism further in the region needs to involve a major development of infrastructure linking the region with Shannon Airport by road and rail. The tourist sector must also expand into new forms of tourism such as archaeological tourism and not become too dependent on the traditional attractions of the West of Ireland.

The second tertiary activity I will discuss is transport. As with most peripheral regions in Europe the transport infrastructure of the west is seriously underdeveloped. This negatively affects all sectors of the economy. The National Development Plan, although beneficial to the West of Ireland, tends to focus the bulk of its major infrastructural projects on the Greater Dublin Area.

Road development is vital to ensure that new economic activities are attracted to the region. The linking of Shannon Airport to the West of Ireland region is vital. An opportunity to do this was recently missed when the western rail corridor was connected to Sixmilebridge, Co. Clare, but not to Shannon Airport which lies a mere 4 km from Sixmilebridge. The government seems reluctant to improve the roads in the region given that no new dual carriageways or motorways are to be constructed in the region in the years to come. The development of the existing airports at Knock and Galway is also essential to the future growth of the region.

LQ 7. Discuss the population dynamics evident in the human environment in an Irish region you have studied.

The region I have studied is the **West of Ireland**. The population of the region reflects how lower levels of economic activity lead to the out-migration of younger people, leaving behind an older workforce in the area. The West of Ireland has a higher dependency ratio than any other part of Ireland. This means that the region has a smaller percentage of its population in the 15–65 age group.

The population density of the region is very low by European standards. In 2002 Counties Mayo, Galway and Roscommon, with 20.3 per cent of the land area of Ireland, contained less than 10 per cent of the population. The total population of the three counties in 2002 was 380,055. The density of population in this period was considerably lower than the national average of 57 per km^2. While the population of the west increased between 1991 and 2002, most of that increase was in the Galway City region. This was due to Galway's success in attracting industry and investment in that period.

A major social problem facing the West of Ireland is the continuing out-migration of the younger population to the Greater Dublin Area. This is due to a number of factors, chiefly the lack of educational opportunities. The west contains only one of Ireland's seven universities and therefore many people are forced to move elsewhere to further their education.

One of the most significant problems currently facing the West of Ireland is the problem of rural depopulation. The continued decline in the numbers working in agriculture and the growth of urban centres such as Galway threatens the future of rural communities in the region. The cycle of rural depopulation found in many areas can lead to a reduction in services such as education, retail, medical and transport services. The National Development Plan has sought to address this problem and organisations were set up under the LEADER programme, which generates employment in rural areas, to reduce rural depopulation. It is also the responsibility of the Western Development Commission and Údarás na Gaeltachta to assist in protecting Ireland's rural environment. The most likely way to slow rural depopulation seems to be the development of a strong tourist sector in the region as tourism is a labour-intensive industry.

Topic **14**
The Greater Dublin Area: A Core Region in Ireland

LQ 1. Draw a sketch map of an Irish region you have studied and on it mark and name the following:

    (a)   The relief of the region
    (b)   The drainage of the region
    (c)   An agricultural area
    (d)   An urban centre
    (e)   An industrial area.

The region I have studied is the **Greater Dublin Area.**

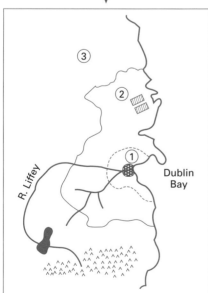

① Dublin city (urban centre)
② Dublin county
③ Greater Dublin Area
▨ Agricultural areas of Lusk/Rush
⋀⋀⋀ Dublin/Wicklow Mountains
▦ Industrial area

R. Liffey

Dublin Bay

Figure 65 The Greater Dublin Area – Ireland's core region

LQ **2. Discuss the physical processes present in an Irish region you have studied.**

The region I have studied is the **Greater Dublin Area**.

The Dublin region experiences a cool temperate maritime **climate** with slightly different characteristics to the climate experienced in the West of Ireland. Precipitation is considerably lower than in the west due to the lower relief and the fact that the region lies in a rain shadow with most Atlantic depressions losing much of their moisture before they reach the region. Precipitation averages 800 mm per annum and is more evenly spread throughout the year than in the west which benefits agriculture. Winter temperatures in the region (3°C) are colder than in the west due to increased distance from the warm North Atlantic Drift. However, summer temperatures (19°C) are higher than in the west and the region experiences more hours of sunshine per day on average. This means that the growing season in the Dublin region is almost 280 days.

Relief in the Greater Dublin Area (GDA) is generally low-lying, which is suited to arable farming and development. The main mountains are the Dublin and Wicklow Mountains in the south and south-west of the region. These mountains were formed during the Caledonian fold movement 400 million years ago when the American plate collided with the Eurasian plate. The highest peak is Glendoo Mountain (586 m). In general, however, the relief consists of undulating lowlands.

With the exception of the mountains, the predominant **soils** are fertile brown-earths. These soils were formed when the area was covered in thick deciduous forest. The forests provided large amounts of leaves which decayed into humus which in turn created a soil suitable for ploughing and arable farming. Soils in mountainous areas are mainly blanket bogs which are suited only to forestry.

The region is **drained** by the River Liffey and smaller rivers such as the Tolka and the Dodder. The River Liffey rises almost 20 km south of Dublin and flows in a large crescent for 130 km before entering the Irish Sea at Dublin Bay. The river is dammed at Poulaphouca, Co. Wicklow to form one of Europe's largest reservoirs.

LQ **3. Discuss the development of primary activities in an Irish region you have studied.**

The region I have studied is the **Greater Dublin Area**. The primary activities I have chosen to discuss are **agriculture and fishing**.

The agricultural sector in the Greater Dublin Area (GDA) is productive and intensive. A number of factors have made the agricultural sector here profitable. These include the fertile brown-earth soils, a favourable climate, level relief and access to both national and international markets.

The dominant form of agriculture in the region is arable farming. This region contains over 1,500 farms and produces almost 12 per cent of Ireland's wheat crop as well as almost 20 per cent of Ireland's potatoes. The fact that the region borders the Irish Sea has a positive influence on the agriculture as it reduces the risk of severe frost and lengthens the growing season. In fact the growing season in the GDA is almost twenty days longer than in parts of the West of Ireland.

As well as arable farming, market gardening is carried out intensively given the proximity of Dublin City as a market for agricultural products. This sector is mainly located in north Co. Dublin where areas such as Lusk and Rush contain hundreds of greenhouses. Some pastoral farming is carried out on land unsuitable for arable farming and the emphasis is on beef production. As a result of the sprawl of urban areas throughout the region much agricultural land has been lost to developers in recent years.

The second primary activity I will discuss is fishing. The fishing sector in this area is, unusually for a core region, quite poorly developed in comparison with the west. This is due to a number of factors both physical and human. The Irish Sea off the coast of this region does not contain the same extensive continental shelf as the Atlantic Ocean does along the west coast. This restricts the growth of plankton and therefore the variety of fish species found in these waters. Pollution levels are also much higher in the Irish Sea due to chemical waste from Ireland and Britain. The impact of foreign trawlers and the introduction of quotas by the European Union have also impacted greatly on the fishing sector.

The main ports in this region are Howth and Skerries. Boats from these ports account for only 3 per cent of total fish caught in Ireland. The main type of fishing in the region is demersal fishing in the lower depths of the sea, as opposed to the pelagic fishing practised in the west. As across Europe, fish stocks are rapidly declining here as a result of over-fishing and driftnet fishing.

4. Discuss the extent to which the physical factors in an Irish region you have studied have assisted the development of a productive agricultural sector in that region.

LQ

The region I have studied is the **Greater Dublin Area**. It is obvious that the physical conditions in this region have assisted the development of the agricultural sector. The agricultural sector in the Greater Dublin Area (GDA) is productive and intensive.

A number of factors have made the agricultural sector here profitable. These include the fertile brown-earth soils, a favourable climate and level relief. Precipitation averages 800 mm per annum and is more evenly spread throughout the year than it is in the West of Ireland, which benefits agriculture. Winter temperatures in the region (3°C) are colder than in the west due to the increased distance from the warm North Atlantic Drift. However, summer temperatures (19°C) are higher than in the west and the region experiences more hours of sunshine per day on average. This means that the growing season in the GDA is almost 280 days.

Relief in the GDA is generally low-lying, which is suited to arable farming and development. With the exception of the mountains, the predominant soils are fertile brown-earths. These soils were formed when the area was covered in thick deciduous forest. The forests provided large amounts of leaves which decayed into humus and created a soil suitable for ploughing and arable farming.

As a result of these favourable physical factors the dominant form of agriculture in the region is arable farming. This region contains over 1,500 farms and produces almost 12 per cent of Ireland's wheat crop as well as almost 20 per cent of Ireland's potatoes. The fact that the region borders the Irish Sea has a positive influence on agriculture as it reduces the risk of severe frost thereby lengthening the growing season. In fact the growing season in the GDA is almost twenty days longer than in parts of the West of Ireland.

As well as arable farming, market gardening is carried out intensively given the proximity of Dublin City as a market for agricultural products. This sector is mainly located in north Co. Dublin and areas such as Lusk and Rush contain hundreds of greenhouses. Some pastoral farming is carried out on land unsuitable for arable farming and the emphasis is on beef production.

LQ 5. Discuss the factors that have led to the development of a productive secondary/manufacturing sector in an Irish region you have studied.

The region I have studied is the **Greater Dublin Area**. The Dublin region has a very strong manufacturing sector. In all, the Greater Dublin Area (GDA) contains over 1,300 individual manufacturing plants. Manufacturing ranges from traditional sectors such as brewing and tobacco to modern industries such as electronics and healthcare. Manufacturing is a major employer in the GDA with almost 100,000 people working in this sector. The region now accounts for 28 per cent of Ireland's industrial output, and wages in the Dublin manufacturing sector are now more than 10 per cent greater than the national average.

The GDA has managed to attract a large number of multinational companies (MNCs) over the past twenty years and now contains almost 800 MNCs, 350 of which are American. The region has become especially attractive to the IT sector, with five of the world's top ten software companies locating their European headquarters in Ireland. Companies such as Intel, Hewlett Packard, IBM and Microsoft now employ almost 12,000 people in the region.

The location of manufacturing in the region has changed considerably in recent decades. During the early stages of Dublin's industrialisation much of the manufacturing was located within the city, some of which remains today such as the Guinness brewery at St James's Gate. However as Ireland modernised in the 1990s the city proved an unattractive destination for manufacturing and most manufacturing is now found in large technology parks on the periphery of the city such as City West.

Dublin is attractive to the manufacturing sector for a number of reasons. It is the country's most important port, which offers easy access to raw materials and provides a convenient means of exporting. The city and substantial hinterland provide a large market for goods such as fashion, processed foods and newspapers. The GDA has a large and educated workforce. Third-level colleges such as Trinity College and UCD provide graduates in fields such as business, marketing, engineering and electronics. Dublin is also the focus of the country's infrastructure, with an international airport and several motorways. Finally, the GDA offers a variety of services to manufacturers such as web design, advertising, accounting and media services.

> **LQ 6. Discuss the development of tertiary activities in an Irish region you have studied.**

The region I have studied is the **Greater Dublin Area**. The **service sector** in the Greater Dublin Area (GDA) employs more people than any other sector. By the end of the twentieth century, service industries accounted for more than 80 per cent of employment in Dublin City. Examples of such service industries are found in the entertainment, commercial, retail, health and education sectors.

The International Financial Services Centre (IFSC) is located in the Docklands area of Dublin City and was developed in order to attract international financial institutions such as Citibank to the region. The project of redeveloping the Docklands area was a huge success and almost 7,000 people are now employed in the financial sector in this area. The investment in the financial sector also created spin-off employment in hotels, taxis, catering, stationery and construction.

The Dublin region is also one of Europe's largest employers in the telesales industry. Many international airline and hotel companies sell ticket and accommodation reservations from their Dublin telesales offices. Examples of such offices are found in East Point Business Park.

The **tourism** sector also contributes greatly to the economy of the GDA. Tourists spend almost €1 billion in Ireland each year and Dublin attracts over 40 per cent of all visitors to Ireland. Dublin's international airport makes it a very accessible location for weekend visitors from the UK and other parts of Europe. Almost 30 million people pass through Dublin Airport each year.

The success of Dublin's tourist sector is due to government investment in leisure facilities such as the National Museum. Also, Dublin City Council's decision to pedestrianise the city's main shopping areas made them more attractive to retailers. The government has invested heavily in marketing Ireland as a tourist destination and Dublin has benefited greatly from this. The growth of newer forms of tourism in Ireland such as golfing holidays has also benefited the Dublin region, which boasts world-class links golf courses at places such as Portmarnock. Business tourism is becoming increasingly important throughout Europe and Ireland's location makes it attractive to investors from the USA. The importance of this type of tourism is reflected in the number of conference centres found in the Dublin area.

LQ   **7. Discuss the population and migratory trends in an Irish region you have studied.**

The region I have studied is the **Greater Dublin Area**. The Greater Dublin Area (GDA) has a large and growing population. Dublin City alone is six times larger than Cork which is Ireland's second largest city. The population of Dublin City is almost 2 million and this does not include the hundreds of thousands of people who live in the surrounding counties of Meath, Louth, Kildare and Wicklow and who commute in and out of the city every day.

The population of the region rose by 10 per cent between 2001 and 2007. Almost 250,000 people immigrated to Ireland during this six-year period, many of whom settled in Dublin. The dominant reason for the rapid population growth of the Dublin region has been in-migration from more peripheral parts of Ireland such as the west. There are numerous reasons for this, most notably educational opportunities. The GDA contains four of Ireland's universities and many young people from other parts of the country have to locate in Dublin to further their education. Also, manufacturing in Ireland is centred on the Dublin region so it offers better employment prospects.

The population structure of the region shows that the GDA has a lower percentage of people (14 per cent) aged over sixty. This is a direct result of the in-migration of a youthful workforce. The rapid population growth and subsequent expansion of the GDA has had many negative effects for the region. The demand for land within the region meant that land values soared. House prices also increased and the rapid growth of suburbs led to large numbers of people commuting to and from the city and hence severe traffic congestion at peak times.

Within Dublin City, different migratory trends can be observed. Until 2000 the population of Dublin County was increasing while the population of Dublin City was falling as people moved out of the city to live in the suburbs. Since 2000 the government has invested millions in urban renewal schemes and there has been a gradual migration of people back into the city centre where problems such as traffic congestion are less severe. Furthermore, a trend of counter-urbanisation has become evident in the Dublin region in recent years as people move to more rural parts of the country in search of a better quality of life.

Topic 15
The Mezzogiorno: A Peripheral Region in Europe

LQ 1. Draw a sketch map of a European region you have studied and on it mark and name the following:

(a) Two physical characteristics of the region
(b) An agricultural region
(c) An industrial region
(d) An urban centre.

The region I have studied is the **Mezzogiorno** in Italy.

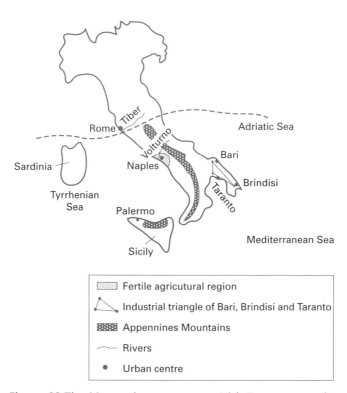

Figure 66 The Mezzogiorno — a non-Irish European region

LQ 2. Discuss the physical processes present in a non-Irish, European region you have studied.

The region I have studied is the **Mezzogiorno**. The Mezzogiorno is made up of the Italian peninsula south of Rome as well as the islands of Sicily and Sardinia. The climate of the Mezzogiorno has contributed to it becoming one of Europe's most peripheral regions.

The Mezzogiorno has a Mediterranean **climate**. This is a two-season climate with mild winters and hot, sunny summers. The climate negatively influences agriculture throughout the region. During summer the north-east trade winds blow over the region. These winds are warm and dry and can lead to drought. Although drought occurs throughout the region, areas such as Sicily are worst affected. The region is also affected by the Sirocco winds which blow up from the Sahara during the summer thus worsening the drought. Summer temperatures average 30°C, while winter temperatures average 16°C. South-westerly winds bring precipitation to the region in winter, which often falls as heavy downpours and can lead to flash floods and mudslides. Precipitation averages 900 mm per year, which would be beneficial to agriculture if it were spread evenly throughout the year however it tends to fall within a period of two or three months.

The Mezzogiorno is characterised by upland **relief**. The Apennines dominate the region and they are vast, rugged mountains formed during the Alpine fold movement 60 million years ago. The Apennines are over 1,200 km long, 130 km wide and up to 1,200 m high. With 80 per cent of the land classified as upland relief, mechanisation of agriculture is difficult. The only areas suitable for both agriculture and settlement are the low-lying coastal plains. Examples of cities found in these areas include Naples, Bari and Taranto. Mount Vesuvius is located on the west coast near Naples.

Soils in the Mezzogiorno are extremely infertile. The only fertile soils in the region are found on the lower slopes of Vesuvius where one finds rich volcanic soils. The climate of the region influences the fertility of the soils. The drought conditions loosen the soils leaving them vulnerable to erosion by winds. The torrential rains can also erode the soils leading to mudslides. It has proved difficult to irrigate soils in the region as much of the underlying bedrock is limestone, which is a permeable rock and therefore allows water to pass through it, making the construction of reservoirs difficult.

The region is **drained** by rivers which flow east into the Adriatic Sea and west into the Tyrrhenian Sea. Examples include the River Volturno, River Agri and River Ofanto.

LQ **3. Discuss the development of primary activities in a non-Irish, European region you have studied.**

The region I have studied is the **Mezzogiorno**. Primary activities in the region include **agriculture** and **fishing**.

Agriculture in the Mezzogiorno has traditionally been unproductive and subsistent, particularly until the 1970s. There are many physical factors that led to agriculture being so unproductive including the mountainous relief, infertile soils and the Mediterranean climate which frequently causes drought. The only productive agricultural areas in the region have traditionally been the alluvial soils near Cerignola and Naples. Also, up until the 1950s most land was owned by absentee landlords who rented the land to tenant farmers. This was called the 'latifundia' system of agriculture and made agriculture extremely unproductive.

The Mezzogiorno has traditionally been isolated from the lucrative north Italian market due to the poor transport links and the mountainous relief between the two regions. This distance from the markets is a major problem for perishable goods.

Throughout the past century there has been a trend of out-migration from the Mezzogiorno to cities such as Milan and Turin in the north. This migration of young people meant that there was no young workforce to take over from ageing farmers which meant many farms were abandoned.

In order to reform the agricultural sector in the Mezzogiorno, the Cassa per il Mezzogiorno was set up in the 1950s. The Cassa invested hugely in agriculture in the region. The large landlord estates were broken up and the land was distributed amongst the farmers, allowing them to adopt more modern methods of agriculture. The Cassa encouraged a change from traditional agriculture to the production of cash crops such as citrus fruits and tobacco. Large amounts of money were invested in irrigation and developing wells and reservoirs to make previously unproductive land productive. Transport links were improved between north and south with the construction of the Italian Autostrade (motorway network), which allows agricultural goods to reach the market quickly.

A second primary activity in the Mezzogiorno is fishing. Although fishing is an important industry for many regions in Western Europe, the enclosed Mediterranean Sea contains relatively high levels of pollution and salinity which limit the variety of fish species in the waters surrounding the Mezzogiorno such as the Adriatic Sea and the Tyrrhenian Sea. These seas also contain low levels of oxygen, and plankton growth is slower here than in the open waters of the Atlantic Ocean.

The dominant fishing ports in the region are areas such as Salerno and Nicastro in the south. There are some factors which have assisted the development of fishing in the region. The peninsula contains a fairly large continental shelf and possesses a large amount of anchovies, tuna and sardines. The weather in the Mezzogiorno is seldom severe, which means fishing can be carried out all year round. The coastline also possesses many natural harbours, particularly along the west coast.

The majority of fish caught are sold for human consumption and as such there are no significant spin-off industries in the form of fish processing. Numerous difficulties face the fishing industry in the Mezzogiorno such as the decline in stocks and the introduction of quotas by the European Union.

LQ	4. Discuss the extent to which the physical processes in a European region you have studied have limited the development of agriculture in that region.

The region I have studied is the **Mezzogiorno**. Agriculture in the Mezzogiorno has traditionally been unproductive and subsistent, particularly until the 1970s. There are many physical factors that led to agriculture being so unproductive, including the mountainous relief, infertile soils and the Mediterranean climate which frequently causes drought.

The climate negatively influences agriculture throughout the region. During summer the north-east trade winds blow over the region. These winds are warm and dry and can lead to drought. The region is also affected by the Sirocco winds, which blow up from the Sahara during the summer thus worsening the drought. Summer temperatures average 30°C, while winter temperatures average 16°C. Precipitation averages 900 mm per year, which would be beneficial to agriculture if it was spread evenly throughout the year however it tends to fall within a period of two or three months.

The Mezzogiorno is characterised by upland relief. With 80 per cent of the land classified as upland relief, mechanisation of agriculture is difficult. The Apennines dominate the region and they are vast, rugged mountains formed during the Alpine fold movement 60 million years ago. Soils in the Mezzogiorno are extremely infertile and unsuitable to arable farming. The drought conditions loosen the soils leaving them vulnerable to erosion by winds. The torrential rains can also erode the soils leading to mudslides. It has proved difficult to irrigate soils in the region as much of the underlying bedrock is limestone, which is a permeable rock and therefore allows water to pass through it, making the construction of reservoirs difficult.

In order to reform the agricultural sector in the Mezzogiorno, the Cassa per il Mezzogiorno was set up in the 1950s. The Cassa has invested hugely in agriculture in the region. The large landlord estates were broken up and the land was distributed amongst the farmers, which allowed them to adopt more modern methods of agriculture. The Cassa encouraged a change from traditional agriculture to the production of cash crops such as citrus fruits and tobacco. Large amounts of money were invested in irrigation and developing wells and reservoirs to make previously unproductive land productive. Transport links with the northern part of Italy were improved with the construction of the Italian Autostrade, which allows agricultural goods to reach the market quickly. Despite the improvements made by the Cassa plan, the physical environment in the Mezzogiorno remains the biggest obstacle to the development of productive agriculture.

> **5.** **Discuss the factors that have limited the development of the**
> **LQ** **manufacturing/secondary sector in a non-Irish, European region you**
> **have studied.**

The region I have studied is the **Mezzogiorno**. Until the 1950s manufacturing was a neglected sector of the economy in the Mezzogiorno. As late as 1965 only 20 per cent of Italy's manufacturing was in the Mezzogiorno, with the majority found in the north of the country. Out-migration was draining the region of its young workforce.

There are many reasons why the region has such low levels of manufacturing. The Mezzogiorno has a lack of raw materials such as coal, with only small supplies of oil and gas. The permeable limestone geology makes the production of hydroelectric power (HEP) difficult. The poor transport infrastructure in the region increases transport costs for industries. Also, the population of the region is small when compared to the core region in the north so industries have a smaller and less-skilled workforce to draw upon. The smaller population also means that there is a smaller domestic market in the region.

From 1957 the Cassa per il Mezzogiorno developed manufacturing in the region in a number of ways. The Cassa selected several growth poles such as Bari, Brindisi and Taranto and focused development on these cities. The Cassa offered incentives to industries to locate in the region such as grants, loans and subsidies. Also, state-owned companies were required to spend 40 per cent of new investment in the Mezzogiorno.

Infrastructure was greatly improved with the creation of the Italian Autostrade, which linked the region with cities in the north such as Milan and Turin.

The industrial development of the region has had both successes and failures. Companies such as Alfa Romeo and Fiat have located in the Mezzogiorno with the latter employing 44,000 workers in the region. Also, Taranto has become home to a strong petrochemical industry, and steelworks are found at Brindisi. In the space of forty years the industrial workforce in the region rose by 300 per cent to 1.4 million. However, large amounts of money granted by the Cassa were squandered or embezzled and not enough emphasis was placed on training and educating the workforce which has resulted in continued out-migration. As the North Italian Plain has continued to develop strongly, there remains a large gap between the north and south of Italy in terms of manufacturing.

> **6.** **The type and level of tertiary activities in a region can vary in terms of**
> **LQ** **their development. Discuss this with reference to one region you have**
> **studied.**

The region I have studied is the **Mezzogiorno**. The tertiary activities I will discuss are **tourism** and **transport**.

Tourism, along with agriculture and manufacturing, has long been seen as a key part of economic development in the Mezzogiorno. The Mezzogiorno has many of the requirements for a successful tourist industry. The region has a rich and varied culture as it was occupied by many civilisations including the Romans, Greeks and Arabs. Numerous historic cities are found in the region such as Pompeii and Herculaneum. As well as cultural attractions the Mezzogiorno has a favourable physical environment for tourism. The climate provides year-round warm temperatures and long hours of sunshine with summer temperatures averaging 30°C. There are numerous scenic coastlines including the Amalfi and Sorrento coasts which contain many sandy beaches.

The Cassa per il Mezzogiorno invested heavily in tourism. The Autostrade motorway system was built to attract tourists from northern Italy and 3,000 hotels were built or refurbished. The changes in the tourist sector were successful along the coastline however the interior of the Mezzogiorno remains underdeveloped.

The second tertiary activity I will discuss is transport. Peripheral regions are characterised by poor transport links which affect the primary, secondary and tertiary sectors' ability to attract investment. From the beginning of the Cassa plan in 1950 to its conclusion in 1984 the government spent €2.5 billion or 20 per cent of the total Cassa funding on transport. Much of this money was spent on developing Italy's Autostrade. The backbone of this system is the Autostrada del Sole which starts in the north near the Swiss border and runs down the west coast to Reggio di Calabria in the toe of Italy. A second motorway services the east coast. As well as motorways, the Cassa developed ports in the Mezzogiorno with the best example being the deep-water port of Taranto.

LQ   **7. Discuss the population and migratory trends found in a non-Irish, European region you have studied.**

The region I have studied is the **Mezzogiorno**. The Mezzogiorno makes up 42 per cent of Italy's land area but contains less than 30 per cent of its population.

During the 1960s the Mezzogiorno suffered a dramatic population decline as millions of people migrated north to the core region near Milan, Turin and Genoa. Emigration to the USA in this period also reduced the population with almost 4 million people emigrating between 1951 and 1971.

There has also been a decrease in the natural rise in population, i.e. births. This is due to the changing role of women, the rising standard of living in the region and the declining influence of the Catholic Church in terms of contraception and abortion.

The consistent out-migration from the Mezzogiorno occurred, and still occurs, because of a number of factors. The unproductive nature of agriculture meant that many young people were reluctant to pursue a career in this sector and instead migrated north. Also, the lack of educational opportunities meant that people of a similar age group were forced to migrate north to further their education.

In recent years population levels in the Mezzogiorno have begun to stabilise. This is due to two factors. The improvements in the economy made by the Cassa per il Mezzogiorno have reduced the need for out-migration. Also, there has been a substantial increase in the number of political refugees from states such as Albania who are seeking asylum in the Mezzogiorno.

Population patterns are similar throughout the Mezzogiorno. These patterns are greatly influenced by the physical landscape. All the major cities in the region are located along the coastal plains in areas such as Campania and Apulia. Examples include Naples, Bari and Brindisi. In these areas population densities are relatively high. However, in the rest of the region, population levels and densities are extremely low. This is mainly due to the mountainous relief and thick forested slopes which make settlement difficult in the interior of the Mezzogiorno. Rural depopulation remains a major problem in the countryside as the poor agricultural sector forces people to migrate to urban centres in order to improve their standard of living.

Topic **16**
The Paris Basin: A Core Region in Europe

LQ

> **1.** Draw a sketch map of a core European region you have studied and on it mark and name the following:
>
>   (a) The relief of the region
>   (b) The drainage of the region
>   (c) An agricultural region
>   (d) An industrial region
>   (e) An urban centre.

The region I have studied is the Paris Basin in France.

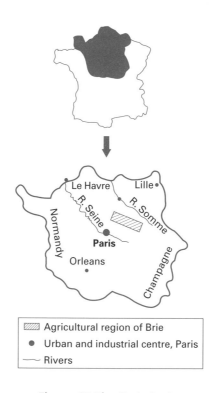

Figure 67 The Paris Basin

LQ 2. Discuss the physical characteristics of a non-Irish, European region you have studied.

The region I have studied is the **Paris Basin**. The Paris Basin occupies almost 25 per cent of France and measures 420 km by 320 km.

The **relief** and **geology** of the Paris Basin are very distinctive and have assisted the development of agriculture. The region represents the syncline or downward part of a fold movement. It consists of layers of sedimentary rocks such as limestone, sandstone and chalk, which were folded downwards by tectonic movement. In the centre are flat layers of limestone and sandstone in the region known as the Île-de-France. As you move out from the centre you encounter relatively steep scarps which are known as côtes. Examples include the Côtes de Meuse and the Côtes de Moselle.

Due to the large size of the Paris Basin, **climatic conditions** vary throughout the region. In the east and north of the region one finds a typically maritime climate dominated by the influence of the North Atlantic Drift. Winds here are south-westerly and these warm, moist winds give mild winters and warm summers. As you move inland towards Paris you encounter a transitional climate, which is a mix of the maritime climate of western Europe and the continental climate of central Europe. Summers here tend to be warmer (24°C) than on the coast, while winters tend to be colder (2°C). Precipitation averages 1,000 mm per annum across the region and is evenly spread throughout the year which benefits agriculture.

Soils throughout the region are generally fertile limon soils which greatly benefits arable farming. Limon soils are stoneless soils which were blown southwards by prevailing winds after the last ice age. The fertile limon soils are the most prevalent but there are also other soils found in the region. Damp clay soils which are suitable for pastoral farming are found in the Île-de-France. In the wine-producing Champagne region infertile chalk soils are found. Finally, in Picardy one finds fertile alluvium deposits which support dairy and arable farming. The Paris Basin is **drained** by the Rivers Seine, Meuse and Somme.

LQ 3. Discuss the development of primary activities in a core European region you have studied.

The core European region I have studied is the **Paris Basin**. Primary activities which are dominant here include **agriculture** and **wine production**.

The Paris Basin is one of the most productive agricultural areas in the European Union. There are a number of factors that account for this. The region has a favourable climate with summer temperatures of 20°C, which is ideal for arable farming. The Basin is also covered with thick limon soils, which are stoneless and easily worked. Large areas of the Basin have a flat or undulating landscape which allows for the use of machinery to increase productivity. Farm sizes are also quite large and industrialised.

Different parts of the Paris Basin have adopted different types of agriculture. In the Île-de-France one finds the main market gardening region, which is centred on the city of Paris. There are two main agricultural areas surrounding Paris: Beauce and Brei. The larger of the two areas is Beauce, which concentrates on the production of arable crops such as barley and maize. Brei is home to the region's dairying sector. The Champagne region, which is found in the east and south-east of the Paris Basin, is divided into wet Champagne and dry Champagne. The soils in dry Champagne are relatively infertile with sheep rearing dominant. Artois and Picardy are composed of vast undulating plains of wheat and barley. In this region the cover of limon on the chalk bedrock has produced France's most fertile soil.

An important aspect of the primary sector in this region is wine production. Wine is France's most famous product. It is a major export and is important to the economy of many regions. While Italy is Europe's largest producer of wine, France is seen to be of greater importance in terms of the quality of its wine. There are a number of wine-producing regions in the Paris Basin such as Burgundy and Champagne. The Burgundy region produces red and white wines and the industry is subject to a rigid quality control system. Champagne is France's most famous wine-producing region and it lies along the eastern edge of the Paris Basin. Expertise in fermentation techniques has given the bubbly wines of Champagne an international reputation. Only wines made in this region can carry the name 'champagne'. The cultivation of vines is a valuable land-use in many areas that would otherwise be non-productive. Spin-off industries in the form of corks and casks and the transport of wines also create valuable employment in rural areas.

LQ **4. Discuss the extent to which the physical characteristics in a European region you have studied have assisted the development of a productive agricultural sector.**

The region I have studied is the **Paris Basin**. It is obvious that the favourable physical characteristics in this region have assisted in the development of its productive agricultural sector.

The Paris Basin is one of the most productive agricultural areas in the European Union. There are a number of factors that account for this. The region has a favourable climate with summer temperatures of 20°C, which is ideal for arable farming. In the east and north of the region one finds a typically maritime climate dominated by the influence of the North Atlantic Drift. The high precipitation associated with this climate has made pastoral farming dominant in this region.

Soils throughout the region are generally fertile limon soils, which greatly benefits arable farming. Limon soils are stoneless soils which were blown southwards by prevailing winds after the last ice age. Despite the prevalence of fertile limon soils, numerous other soils are found in the region. Damp clay soils which are suitable for pastoral farming are found in the Île-de-France. In the wine-producing Champagne region infertile chalk soils are found. Finally, in Picardy one finds fertile alluvium deposits which support dairy and arable farming.

The relief and geology of the Paris Basin is very distinctive and has assisted the development of agriculture. The region represents the syncline or downward part of a fold movement. The predominantly level relief assists agriculture as it allows for easy use of machinery.

The varying physical characteristics mentioned above have led to various forms of agriculture being practised throughout the Paris Basin. In the Île-de-France one finds the main market gardening region, which is centred on the city of Paris. There are two main agricultural areas surrounding Paris: Beauce and Brei. The larger of the two areas is Beauce, which concentrates on the production of arable crops such as barley and maize. Brei is the home to the region's dairying sector. The Champagne region, which is found in the east and south-east of the Paris Basin, is divided into wet Champagne and dry Champagne. The soils in dry Champagne are relatively infertile with sheep rearing dominant. Artois and Picardy are composed of vast undulating plains of wheat and barley. In this region the cover of limon on the chalk bedrock has produced France's most fertile soil.

> **5.** **Discuss the factors that have led to the development of a well-developed manufacturing/secondary sector in a non-Irish, European region you have studied.**
>
> LQ

The region I have studied is the **Paris Basin**. The economy of France is centred on Paris and its surrounding hinterland, the Île-de-France. There are a number of factors which account for the industrial importance of the region, the most important of which is accessibility.

Paris is accessible by air, rail and water. Paris is the focal point of a major inland canal system allowing industry to import and export its raw materials and finished products. Paris itself is connected by the River Seine to the sea at Le Havre. The city of Paris is a busy port which handles both imports and exports. Paris is also the focus of the French road and rail networks. The central position of the city makes it accessible from all corners of France.

The huge population of Paris (11 million) provides both a labour force for industry as well as a market for all the goods manufactured in the region. The city of Paris and its hinterland contain 25 per cent of the French workforce. The rich agricultural sector has also benefited manufacturing in the form of spin-off industries such as agricultural machinery, food processing and fertilisers. These spin-off industries have allowed previously rural areas such as Picardy to become more industrialised. Furthermore, the central position which France enjoys in Europe allows access to many international markets.

There are numerous types of industry found in the Paris Basin. The most well-known aspect of the manufacturing sector is the fashion industry. This industry has been present in Paris for centuries and has spawned several spin-off industries such as jewellery and perfume. Traditional industries such as these are found west of the Louvre and in the south of the city. Heavy industries tend to be concentrated in the north-east of the city. Many of these factories are located on canals to allow transportation of bulky raw materials such as petrochemicals. Examples of such industries include Renault, Citroën and pharmaceutical industries such as Akzo NV.

Modern industries tend to be located outside the city of Paris in suburbs such as Marne-la-Vallée. This is a modern suburb that was constructed as part of the Schema Directeur, which was a policy to control the spread of Paris into its hinterland. Industries found in suburbs such as these include electronics, food processing and consumer appliances. The growth of Paris as an industrial centre has created numerous problems. Because of its growth, other areas in the region have been neglected, which has led to out-migration from these regions and overcrowding and traffic congestion in Paris.

LQ **6. Discuss the development of tertiary activities in a non-Irish, European region you have studied.**

The region I have studied is the **Paris Basin**. The tertiary activities I will discuss are **transport** and **tourism**.

The transport infrastructure of this region is extremely well developed and yet faces many of the problems associated with cities in the developed world such as traffic congestion. The city of Paris and indeed the entire Paris Basin is the focal point of all road and rail routes in France. The level relief of the region has facilitated the development of large-scale infrastructural projects, particularly railways.

The most popular mode of transport in the region is the TGV rail network. This system was initiated in the 1970s and links Paris to other French cities such as Marseille, Perpignan and Nantes. The TGV also links the region to other parts of Europe such as London (via the Channel Tunnel), Munich and Brussels. This rail network allows trains to move at speeds of up to 300 km per hour.

Within the region numerous, smaller modes of transport exist. For example the Métro, RER, bus and tram systems provide a linked rail, underground and road transport network that allows the efficient movement of people around the city of Paris and its suburbs. There are approximately 7,400 buses in the city of Paris alone. All of these aspects of public transport are administered by the Paris Transportation Authority known as Syndicat des transports d'Île-de-France (STIF).

In spite of the fact that rail transport throughout the region is so well developed, more than one-third of all commuters to the city travel by car. This obviously causes traffic congestion and in an attempt to alleviate this, two major motorways were constructed around the city. The inner ring was named the Boulevard Périphérique and the outer ring is known simply as the A86.

The second tertiary activity I will discuss is tourism. The focal point of the tourist sector in the region is obviously the city of Paris. Paris receives 28 million tourists and business travellers each year, making tourism a vital part of the region's economy. The 'City of Lights' attracts this volume of tourists due to the wide variety of attractions it contains, most notably the Eiffel Tower. This steel structure built alongside the River Seine attracts 5.5 million people alone each year. Other attractions include the Arc de Triomphe built in 1806, the Grand Arche in La Defense, Notre Dame cathedral and the Champs-Elysées. After the Eiffel Tower the most popular attraction is the Louvre. This is the world's largest museum and contains famous works of art such as Leonardo da Vinci's *Mona Lisa* and *Madonna of the Rocks*.

Less artistic attractions include Stade de France, an 80,000-seat stadium which holds rugby and football internationals, and Roland Garros which is home to the French Open. The beauty, cuisine and shopping of Paris are also responsible for the high tourist numbers each year.

LQ **7. Discuss the population and migratory patterns present in a non-Irish, European region you have studied.**

The region I have studied is the **Paris Basin**. This has traditionally been France's core region and as such the centre of population for many centuries. The size of the region's population has risen consistently since the end of World War II.

The dominant population pattern in the region has been one of in-migration. This pattern is not uncommon in most European regions, however in the Paris Basin it has a notable ethnic element. In many core regions in-migration is common from more peripheral parts of the country, and this is also the case in the Paris Basin with large numbers of migrants from areas such as the Massif Central. Allied to this, however, one finds mass in-migration from parts of north Africa such as Algeria and Morocco. This trend originated in the labour migration of the 1960s, when many employers found manpower in north African villages. In this period over 1.6 million workers migrated from Algeria, Tunisia and Morocco. The trend continued in the 1970s as many French colonials returned from states such as Cambodia. In 1973, however, laws were passed which were intended to reduce this migration and by the 1980s the Paris Basin had ceased to be a place of mass immigration.

Today it is estimated that 8 per cent of the population of the Paris Basin is composed of foreign-born immigrants. This history of immigration has had obvious effects on the cultural make-up of the region, both in terms of religion and ethnicity. Although the dominant religion is Roman Catholic, there are over 2.5 million Muslims living in the Paris Basin. There are also large African and Arab neighbourhoods in the Paris suburbs. Feelings of discrimination among these groups have often led to social unrest, as was the case in November 2005. The race riots seen throughout the Paris suburbs at that time were amongst the worst in over fifty years and stemmed from the growing isolation of, and feelings of discrimination among, minority groups.

Topic **17**
India: A Non-European/Sub-Continental Region

LQ 1. Draw a sketch map of a continental/sub-continental region you have studied and on it mark and name the following:

(a) The relief of the region
(b) The drainage of the region
(c) An urban centre
(d) An agricultural region
(e) An industrial centre
(f) A major port.

The region I have studied is **India**.

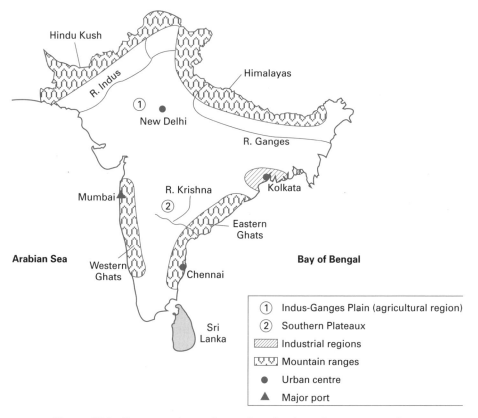

Figure 68 India — a sub-continental region/non-European region

LQ 2. **Discuss the physical characteristics of a non-European region you have studied.**

The region I have studied is **India**. The physical characteristics of the region include **relief**, **climate**, **soils** and **drainage**. Relief in India can be divided into three areas: the northern mountains, the Indus-Ganges Plain and the southern plateaux.

The northern mountains form a natural border between India and the rest of Asia. Mountains extend from the Hindu Kush range in the north-west to the Himalayas in the north-east. These mountains contain the world's highest peak, Mount Everest, as well as the next twenty-four highest peaks. The mountains were formed during the Alpine fold movement 60 million years ago when the Indian plate moved north and collided with the Eurasian plate.

The Indus-Ganges Plain represents the syncline of the fold movement which formed the Himalayas. It is a deep depression which contains the Rivers Indus and Ganges. Due to melting glaciers in the mountains during summer, these rivers flood over an extensive area, depositing large amounts of fertile alluvium. Due to these fertile deposits, over half of India's population lives in this region.

The southern plateaux are found in the south of the country and the largest is the Deccan Plateau. It tilts from west to east and rivers such as the Krishna drain across it into the Bay of Bengal. Smaller mountain ranges called the Western and Eastern Ghats are found near coastal lowlands in this area.

The climate of India is tropical continental monsoon and can be divided into two seasons: the dry monsoon and the wet monsoon. The dry monsoon lasts from October to May and occurs as a result of cold or warm winds which blow outwards from central Asia. Because these winds originate over land they are extremely dry and any moisture that they do contain falls as snow over the Himalayas. The dry monsoon often leads to severe drought.

The wet monsoon occurs from June to September when warm ocean winds blow south-westerly and south-easterly across India. These winds pass over the Ghats leading to large amounts of relief rain, which can be as high as 1,000 mm in six weeks. By the time the winds reach the north-west they are dry leading to desert conditions there (Thar Desert).

The soils in the region are influenced by the relief, drainage and climate. Alluvial soils are found on the floodplains of the many large rivers. Laterites or red soils are found throughout the country. These are soils in which all minerals except iron have been leached to lower horizons. Black soils are found in the Deccan Plateau and these retain moisture easily and are used for the growth of cotton.

LQ **3. Discuss the development of primary activities in a continental/sub-continental region you have studied.**

The region I have studied is **India**. The primary activities I will discuss are **agriculture** and **fishing**.

Agriculture in India has traditionally been intensive subsistent farming. This means that farm sizes are generally small (0.5 hectares) and that most farmers only produce enough to sustain themselves. The nature of agriculture in India is greatly influenced by the climate, soils and relief of the country and productive agriculture is only practised where the physical environment is favourable.

India's cultivated land is equal to the total cultivated land of the European Union. Two-thirds of India's one billion people depend directly on the land for their living. Arable farming is the main form of agriculture. Rice is the main crop and 25 per cent of agricultural land is covered in this cereal. In the past almost all planting and harvesting was done by hand, which made the agricultural sector extremely unproductive.

The rapid growth of India's population over the past century has placed enormous pressure on the agricultural sector. In order to meet this challenge, genetically modified, high-yield varieties of rice have been introduced. This rice is resistant to many diseases. This modernisation of India's agricultural sector has been referred to as the 'Green Revolution' and has led to India becoming a net exporter of food. The pastoral sector remains underdeveloped as the slaughter of cattle is illegal in many states due to the Hindu belief that the cow is a sacred animal.

The second primary activity I will discuss is fishing. Fish production has increased more than fivefold since Indian independence. It rose from only 800,000 tons in 1950 to 4.1 million tons in the early 1990s. Special efforts have been made to support inland fishing, fish farming, coastal fishing and deep sea fishing. Coastal fish production alone increased from 520,000 tons in 1950 to 2.1 million tons in 1990. The important saltwater fish species for the industry are mackerel, sardines, shark, sole, tuna and prawns. The dominant freshwater fish are carp and catfish.

There are roughly 1.7 million full-time fishermen, 1.3 million part-time fishermen and 2.3 million occasional fishermen who also work as ferrymen or salt makers. It is estimated that the fishing fleet consists of 180,000 sail or oar craft, 26,000 motorised craft and 34,000 mechanised boats. Apart from the main harbours of Kochi, Madras and Calcutta there are 23 minor fishing harbours and 95 fish landing centres.

Great potential exists for expanding India's fishing industry. In the mid-1990s only 33 per cent of India's waters (2 million km^2) were being fished. It is estimated that 4.5 million tons of fish are available to be fished in the waters that remain. The government is greatly supportive of fishing and provides subsidies to poor fishermen to enable them to motorise their craft and increase their catch.

4.	**Discuss the extent to which climate and relief have influenced the development of agriculture in a non-European region you have studied.**
LQ	

The region I have studied is **India**. It is obvious that both climate and relief have greatly influenced the development of agriculture in this region. Agriculture in India has traditionally been intensive subsistent farming. This means that farm sizes are generally small (0.5 hectares) and that most farmers only produce enough to sustain themselves. The nature of agriculture in India is greatly influenced by the climate and relief of the country, and productive agriculture is only practised where the physical environment is favourable.

Relief in India can be divided into three areas: the northern mountains, the Indus-Ganges Plain and the southern plateaux. Each area displays distinct forms of agriculture as a result of the relief. The mountains in the north prohibit any type of productive agriculture. The Indus-Ganges Plain is home to the country's agricultural sector. It is a deep depression which contains the Rivers Indus and Ganges. Due to melting glaciers in the mountains during summer, these rivers flood over an extensive area depositing large amounts of fertile alluvium. Due to these fertile deposits, over half of India's population live in this region. Agriculture in the southern plateaux is limited to cotton and some rice fields.

Two-thirds of India's one billion people depend directly on the land for their living. Arable farming is the main form of agriculture and is only practised in areas where the climate and relief are suitable. Rice is the main crop and 25 per cent of agricultural land is covered in this cereal. In the past almost all planting and harvesting was done by hand, which made the agricultural sector extremely unproductive.

The rapid growth of India's population in the past century has placed enormous pressure on the agricultural sector. In order to meet this challenge, genetically modified, high-yield varieties of rice have been introduced. This rice is resistant to many diseases. This modernisation of India's agricultural sector has been referred to as the 'Green Revolution' and has led to India becoming a net exporter of food.

LQ 5. **Discuss the development of the manufacturing sector in a non-European region you have studied.**

The region I have studied is **India**. India's manufacturing sector has developed rapidly since the country gained independence from Britain in 1947. At that time, only 2 per cent of the labour force was employed in industry, and almost all industry was concentrated in the three main cities of Bombay (Mumbai), Calcutta (Kolkata) and Madras (Chennai).

Since independence a number of factors have helped India's programme of industrialisation. The population of over one billion people provides a large domestic market and workforce. As well as this the country has some important natural resources such as coal and iron ore. Finally, the large agricultural sector has led to the development of agri-industries such as fertilisers, machinery and food processing.

One of the main factors in India's favour in recent years has been the low wages which multinational companies can pay employees in the country. This has resulted in many such companies relocating to India from countries such as Ireland where minimum wages are in place. This has hugely benefited the emerging Indian economy, particularly in terms of the many call centres locating in the country. As well as this relatively unskilled work, India is also increasingly attracting companies as a result of its skilled workforce. India now produces more university graduates per year than the USA and Canada combined.

Industry is still concentrated in four main regions in India. In Kolkata one finds India's traditional industries of cotton, clothing and textiles. Being close to the country's deposits of coal and iron ore also means that most of India's heavy industries are found here, e.g. iron and steelworks.

Chennai, in the south, concentrates on light engineering industries with hundreds of software companies locating in Bangalore. This region is often called 'India's silicon valley'.

In the west of India, Mumbai is the centre of industry. While traditional industries such as food processing remain important, this region has attracted many foreign companies involved in growth sectors such as electronics and pharmaceuticals. This indicates the increasingly modern nature of India's manufacturing sector.

The final industrial region is in Ahmadabad in the north-west where one finds chemical and engineering companies.

LQ 6. **Discuss the development of tertiary activities in a continental/sub-continental region you have studied.**

The region I have studied is **India**. The tertiary activities I will discuss are **transport** and **tourism**.

Although the transport infrastructure in India remains severely underdeveloped in places, huge advances have been made in this sector since the country gained independence. The dominant mode of transport is rail and India contains the longest rail network of any country in the world. The average rail trip is 60 km long and there is over 64,000 km of track. India is linked with Bangladesh by rail for freight purposes but has no rail link with China.

After rail, bus is the preferred mode of transport. Like rail, bus companies are state run. Long-distance travel is common, with journeys often over 500 km. Recently newer buses and improvements in roads have made these journeys more bearable. Today there are officially 65,569 km of highways, however in poorer areas these are of very poor quality. Improvements in roads are vital as the number of car users is increasing each year. In 2002, 50,000 new cars were bought in New Delhi alone.

The waterways were once used for both travel and trade but today they are largely redundant. The ports are the dominant gateway for trade as they handle 95 per cent of all imports and exports by quantity and 77 per cent by value. The main ports are Kolkata, Haldia, Paradip and Chennai.

The rapid economic growth in India in the past fifty years has made air transport accessible to a wider percentage of the population. Air India is the dominant airline and carries 135 aircraft. Other airlines include Air Deccan and Kingfisher.

The Indian sub-continent offers a wealth of attractions for tourists and has possibly the most diverse range of attractions of any country in the world. The physical attractions vary hugely from north to south. In the extreme north one finds the spectacular slopes of the Himalayas. The lower slopes of the mountains offer opportunities for skiing, though this is an underdeveloped sector. In the south of the country one finds the opportunity for spectacular safari tours east and west of the Deccan Plateau and this is a rapidly growing sector of tourism.

As well as physical attractions India boasts many cultural, religious, historical and architectural sights, such as the Taj Mahal at Agra. High-class tourism can also be seen at exclusive coastal resorts such as those found in Goa.

Despite these attractions, the tourism industry in India remains underdeveloped and investment is needed at all levels to ensure the growth of this labour-intensive sector.

LQ **7. Discuss the characteristics of the human environment in a non-European region you have studied.**

The region I have studied is **India**. The human environment is evident here in terms of population, religion and culture.

The population of India in 2007 was estimated at 1,129,866,154 people. This made India only the second country in the world to pass the one billion inhabitants mark and made it the second most populated country in the world behind China. The fact that India's population rose by 21.34 per cent between 1991 and 2001 indicates how rapid this growth has been. The sex ratio (number of females per thousand males) of population is 933. Although India occupies only 2.4 per cent of the world's land area, it supports over 15 per cent of the world's population. Almost 40 per cent of Indians are under the age of fifteen.

There are numerous factors which account for India's rapidly growing population, most notably a high birth rate coupled with a rapidly declining death rate. The high birth rates were often attributed to lack of education in terms of family planning, however as India progressed into a developed country throughout the twentieth century birth rates remained high. This suggests that India's high birth rates occur as a result of tradition and culture rather than a lack of education. The declining death rates have occurred as India has become more developed and improved its healthcare system as well as sanitation. This has helped increase life expectancy. While India was a predominantly rural nation for centuries, in recent decades it has become increasingly urbanised as the employment prospects are brighter in urban areas which also contain a greater variety of services.

Over thousands of years of history, India has been invaded from Central Asia, Arabia, Afghanistan and the West. As a result Indian people have developed a remarkable racial and cultural identity. Religion, caste and language greatly influence one's role in Indian society. The Indian government officially recognises eighteen languages, with Hindi being the most commonly used. In terms of religion, 83 per cent of the population are Hindu, however India is also home to more than 120 million Muslims. The population also includes Christians, Sikhs and Buddhists. The caste system plays a vital role in Indian society. Traditionally there are four categories of caste including a category of outcastes which were known as untouchables but are now called Dalits. Within the four broad categories there are thousands of castes and sub-castes which determine one's social standing.

Topic **18**
The European Union (EU)

The most likely short question on the EU will ask you to identify the Member States on a map and state the years in which they joined.

Figure 69 EU Member States

Year joined	Member State
1957	Original members: France, Italy, Germany, Netherlands, Belgium and Luxembourg
1973	Ireland, the UK and Denmark
1981	Greece
1986	Spain and Portugal
1995	Austria, Finland and Sweden
2004	Estonia, Latvia, Lithuania, Poland, Czech Republic, Slovakia, Hungary, Slovenia, Cyprus and Malta
2007	Bulgaria and Romania

LQ 1. **Discuss the impact which the recent expansions of the EU will have on Member States with reference to one state you have studied.**

The Member State I have studied is **Ireland**. The enlargement and expansion of the EU has presented both problems and opportunities for existing Member States, for example in relation to economic and sovereignty issues.

Although the EU has consistently grown since its beginnings in 1957, the most recent expansions have been very significant. In 2004 Estonia, Latvia, Lithuania, Poland, Czech Republic, Slovakia, Hungary, Slovenia, Malta and Cyprus joined and they were followed in 2007 by Romania and Bulgaria. These new Member States are predominantly peripheral or underdeveloped regions and as such will be net beneficiaries rather than net contributors to EU funding. As a result funding which had previously been directed to peripheral regions such as the West of Ireland may now be redirected towards these countries. Funding granted through the EU Structural Funds is used to improve infrastructure and create employment in the more peripheral parts of the EU.

The new EU members have a much higher dependence on agriculture (28.8 per cent) than exists in the other EU countries (5.5 per cent) and their accession increases the number of farmers in the EU by 300 per cent. While numbers employed in agriculture in these countries are high, agriculture is poorly developed and the modernisation of agriculture will divert huge funds from the Common Agricultural Policy (CAP). This may reduce the amount of subsidies received by Irish farmers. Furthermore, the additional agricultural output will increase competition for Irish farmers and may see prices fall.

The recent expansion of the EU has had many positive effects on Ireland. With the growth of the Irish economy in recent years and the increasingly educated and skilled nature of the workforce, there has been a significant lack of unskilled workers in the tertiary sector. This gap has been filled by migrants from new Member States such as Poland. These migrants are needed to sustain economic growth in industries such as hotels, pubs, shops and construction. Furthermore, many skilled migrants have also filled gaps in Ireland's labour force in sectors such as nursing. Finally, the new Member States offer indigenous Irish companies the opportunity for investment and also represent a new market for Irish goods and services.

Although the expansion of the EU has consistently benefited Ireland, its continued growth has meant a reduction in Ireland's sovereignty. The four main institutions in the EU which make decisions and laws are: the European Commission, European Parliament, Council of Ministers and European Council. In the past thirty years these organisations have exerted an increasing influence over Ireland. This can be seen in terms of Ireland's current currency and interest rates as set by the European Central Bank. One area where controversy is likely to arise is foreign policy, where suggestions for a common defence force are at odds with Ireland's neutral status.

LQ **2.** **Discuss the effect which membership of the EU has had on (the economy of) any one country you have studied.**

The country I have studied is **Ireland**. Ireland became a member of the EU (then the EEC) in 1973. EU membership has had a profound influence on the social and economic development of Ireland.

When Ireland joined the EU it was one of Europe's most peripheral countries, not just in terms of location but in terms of economic development. It was a predominantly agricultural economy and rural country with a large percentage of its national income based on agricultural exports. Because of this, one of the main motivating factors for Ireland joining the EU was the promise of price protection for farmers under the Common Agricultural Policy (CAP).

The CAP was designed to ensure that prices for products such as beef and milk never fell below a certain level. To ensure this was the case the EU would buy surplus amounts of beef and milk and store them rather than release them onto the open market where an excess of one product would cause its price to fall. Although this led to some controversy over 'beef mountains' and 'milk lakes', Irish farmers benefited nonetheless.

Another aspect of EU membership that has benefited Irish farmers is that they now have a large market of Member States to sell their products to. In the past, most of Ireland's agricultural exports had been to the UK.

Membership of the EU also meant that Irish fishermen signed up to the Common Fisheries Policy (CFP). Many Irish fishermen would argue that they have not received the same economic benefits that farmers experienced under the CAP. The main reason for this is that Ireland's membership coincided with the recognition that European fish stocks were in rapid decline due to over-fishing. Because of this the EU introduced quotas which greatly limited the amount of fish that could be landed. Also, the CFP meant that Ireland had to open its waters to trawlers from other EU countries at certain times of the year and this led to many conflicts between Irish and Spanish trawlers.

Apart from agriculture and fishing, Ireland has received funding for large-scale infrastructural developments from the European Regional Development Fund and funding for educational initiatives from the European Social Fund. It is likely that much of the prosperity which Ireland enjoys as a result of the Celtic Tiger economy of the 1990s is due in no small part to membership of the EU. A price has had to be paid for this and in the process we lost some of our ability to legislate for ourselves (our sovereignty).

Changes in the Boundaries of Regions over Time

1. 'The boundaries of regions can change greatly over time.' Discuss this statement with reference to a European example you have studied.

The region I have studied is **Germany**. Germany provides a classic example of the changing nature of regional boundaries. Throughout the late nineteenth century and the twentieth century the German nation varied greatly in terms of its size and influence. Indeed the area now known as Germany had many different names during that period.

In the late nineteenth century the German Empire and its neighbour the Austro–Hungarian Empire covered the majority of Central Europe. However disagreement between these two empires led to the Great War, or World War I, which lasted from 1914 to 1918. The collapse of the Central Powers in the autumn of 1918 and the subsequent peace treaties brought about major border changes across Europe. The dismemberment of the Austro–Hungarian Empire and the disarmament of and imposition of reparation payments on the German Empire completely altered the map of Europe. Furthermore, at the Paris Peace Conference at Versailles, the boundaries of what was now called Germany were changed to facilitate the emergence of new states such as Poland and Czechoslovakia.

The Treaty of Versailles provided what seemed like the basis for stability in Europe, however the redrawing of Germany's boundaries laid the foundations for World War II. As a result of the border changes millions of Germans were living in other countries such as Poland. These people identified with their German neighbours and had no wish to be part of another country. This mood of disquiet, coupled with a general mood of dissatisfaction throughout Germany as a result of war reparations and the country's inability to build an army, allowed a powerful orator called Adolf Hitler to come to power.

Hitler's stated ambition was to unify all Germans, however his motives were far more expansionist and he led Germany into World War II in September 1939. During this war the boundaries of Germany briefly stretched across much of Europe as the armies of the Third Reich swept

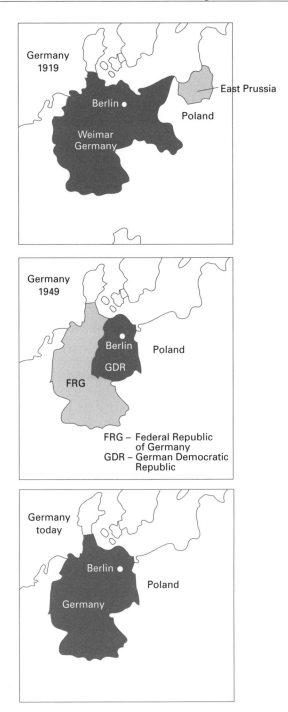

Figure 70 The changing boundaries of Germany

all before them. Eventually in 1945 the war ended in defeat for Germany and the country was to have its boundaries changed again.

With the Allies, and Russia in particular, determined to keep Germany weak, the country was divided in two in 1949. East Germany was to be administered by communist Russia; while West Germany was to be allowed to develop under the guidance of the Western powers. Over the next forty years West Germany developed into a modern industrial economy; while East Germany stagnated.

Finally in 1989 Mikhail Gorbachev, a reforming Russian leader, renounced Russia's claim to East Germany and the reunification of the two parts took place. There now existed a single German state for the first time in almost half a century. It is obvious therefore that Germany provides a good example as to how the boundaries of regions can change over time.

LQ **2. Discuss the extent to which the boundaries of an Irish region you have studied have changed over time.**

The region I have studied is the **Gaeltacht regions** in Ireland. Gaeltacht regions are parts of Ireland where over 60 per cent of the population speak Irish as their first language. Throughout recent centuries the amount of people speaking Irish as their first language has both risen and fallen, therefore the boundaries of Gaeltacht regions have varied greatly.

In 1850 over 1.6 million people spoke Irish and the language was in everyday use, particularly in the West of Ireland. However, by the early twentieth century this figure had fallen to almost half a million. This shrinking of Gaeltacht regions was due to many factors, not least the enduring influence of the Plantations. The Plantations were a method used by the British to erode the culture in Ireland. They involved the granting of large amounts of land to British landlords in Ireland, thereby forcing locals who needed to engage with them to use the English language.

A second factor which contributed to the decline of the Irish language in this period was the large-scale emigration from Ireland which occurred from the fifteenth to the late twentieth centuries. This emigration took place mainly from the West of Ireland, which was and is the heartland of Irish-speaking communities.

Although they had shrunk considerably until the early twentieth century, Gaeltacht regions in Ireland were to expand briefly in the period around independence. On gaining independence from Britain there was a surge of nationalism facilitated by government policy. From the 1930s

Irish was the first official language of the state. Irish was, and remains, a compulsory subject in schools throughout first- and second-level education and Irish became a requirement for people seeking jobs in the civil service. These measures saw a brief expansion in the boundaries of Gaeltacht regions throughout the early to mid-twentieth century.

Since the mid-twentieth century the use of Irish as an everyday language has diminished rapidly. There are numerous reasons for this, most notably the influence of modern media. Today most forms of media such as newspapers, television, radio and the Internet are conducted through English. Furthermore, the continued out-migration of young people from the West of Ireland to Dublin has meant that fewer children are being raised as Irish speakers. Today only 51 per cent of 3–5 year olds in Gaeltacht regions speak Irish, which indicates that the boundaries of these regions will continue to decline in the future.

There have been numerous attempts to arrest the decline of the Irish language in recent decades. The main successes have been the Irish television channel TG4 and to a lesser extent the Irish radio station Raidió na Gaeltachta. Gaeltacht regions also received a boost in 2005 when the European Union granted official status to the language.

The government has recognised that in order to preserve the Irish language it must reduce out-migration from Gaeltacht areas by stimulating the economy of the regions. The Department of Community, Rural and Gaeltacht Affairs has responsibility for economic development in these areas. Údarás na Gaeltachta is an organisation that was set up in order to create jobs in Gaeltacht regions and to date has created over 8,100 full-time and over 3,500 part-time jobs. Despite this, the language continues to decline.

LQ **3. Discuss the extent to which the boundaries of urban regions can change over time with reference to one example you have studied.**

The urban region I have studied is **Dublin City**. Dublin was not always the sprawling urban centre it is today and its boundaries have expanded greatly over the past century, particularly since the 1980s.

Dublin was little more than a large town in 1950 and its rapid growth was initially due to the availability of employment. This attracted migrants from the peripheral West of Ireland, a trend which continues today. This in-migration of a young workforce led to a growth in Dublin's population. Faced with a burgeoning population, city planners attempted to control the inevitable sprawl of housing which was to occur. They did this by constructing new towns on the periphery of the city to act as commuter towns. These towns included Tallaght,

Clondalkin and Blanchardstown. Although intended to control sprawl these towns eventually became part of the city as it spread outwards into neighbouring counties.

As Ireland became increasingly prosperous towards the end of the twentieth century large numbers of multinational companies were attracted to the country, and in particular to the Dublin area which offered good infrastructure and a young, educated workforce. These companies could not locate in older parts of the city, which were unsuitable, and so they located in large technical and industrial estates on the periphery of the city (such as City West), which only served to further the city's growth. As well as this, new hotels and housing estates continued to spring up in order to cater for the increasing amounts of commuters to the city. Such developments took place in areas as far away as Navan, Co. Meath and Arklow, Co. Wicklow.

The rapid growth of Dublin in the past few decades has had many consequences. The lack of land within the city for housing means that house prices in the region are over €100,000 more expensive than in other parts of the country. Furthermore, the increasing amount of commuters has placed pressure on infrastructure with massive traffic jams common at peak times. There have been many attempts to ease this congestion, for example the construction of the LUAS light railway lines, the development of the M50 motorway and the construction of the Port Tunnel. Transport 21 outlines plans for further infrastructural projects to cater for the rapidly expanding boundaries of Dublin City.

Topic **20**
Political and Cultural Tensions

The region I have studied is **India**. India was colonised by European traders for centuries and by the mid-nineteenth century was under British control. At that time India was made up of present-day India, Pakistan and Bangladesh. The British encouraged conflict between the two dominant religious groups in the region: Hindus and Muslims. Finally, after independence in 1949, two new states were created based on this religious divide. India became a Hindu state and Pakistan became a Muslim state.

As a result of this political division, large numbers of minority religious groups were left in both countries. This led to rioting and large-scale migration. More than 15 million people migrated across the Hindu Kush, many of whom died. Pakistan was based on the Muslim population living on the Indus and Ganges river systems. As a result, this state was split into two parts separated by a long distance, with northern India in between. This was not practical and in 1971 Eastern Pakistan became Bangladesh. Tensions remain high between India and Pakistan, especially over the disputed territory of Kashmir.

After independence, violent fighting broke out in the Kashmir valley on the border of India and Pakistan between the minority (25 per cent) Hindu population and the majority (75 per cent) Muslim population in the region. This was to result in war between the newly formed states. The United Nations negotiated a ceasefire and established a line of control for each country, which was intended to be temporary but which has remained as a dividing line between the two cultural groups. Today India controls about 80 per cent of the Kashmiri population, including large numbers of Muslims. This situation is unacceptable to Pakistan, which wants to gain control of the River Indus and several of its large tributaries which originate in the disputed region. As both India and Pakistan have nuclear weapons, this remains a potentially dangerous situation, culturally and politically.

Figure 71 India, Pakistan and Bangladesh

LQ 2. **With reference to an Irish example you have studied, discuss how political problems can both create and result from cultural division.**

The region I have studied is **Northern Ireland**. Throughout the past number of centuries religious differences have led to political strife in this region. The causes of these religious differences date back centuries and yet the ramifications are still being felt today.

By the time Ireland obtained a measure of independence from Britain in the 1920s with the establishment of the Irish Free State and Northern Ireland, distinct cultural differences could be observed on the island. The Free State, later to become the Republic of Ireland, was composed almost exclusively of Catholics. The six counties of Northern Ireland however showed a much more diverse culture: two-thirds Protestant and one-third Catholic.

The origin of this division was in part the Plantations which had taken place centuries earlier. The British, in an attempt to solidify their hold on Ireland, invited Protestant landowners from Scotland and England to take land in Ireland. This was very effective in Ulster, where large numbers of these landlords migrated in the 1600s. This created tensions between the indigenous Catholics and the Protestant settlers which became violent on numerous occasions.

With the establishment of the Irish Free State, calls from the Catholic community (nationalists) for a united Ireland were met with fierce opposition from the Protestant community (unionists). From the 1920s until the late 1960s these differences, while still present, were not particularly violent. This may have been due to the economic prosperity the north was enjoying as a result of strong trade links with Britain. However by the 1960s the Catholic population was being discriminated against by the ruling Protestant majority and many civil rights marches descended into extreme violence. This led to the formation of illegal paramilitary groups on both sides and a period of unspeakable violence called 'the Troubles' which lasted over thirty years. During this period political relations between Northern Ireland and the Republic of Ireland were extremely poor, with many people in the Republic urging their government to intercede with force in favour of the Catholics in the north. Trade between the countries was non-existent.

Finally in 1998 the Good Friday Agreement, signed by the British and Irish governments, formed the basis for lasting peace. Further progress has taken place in recent years with the establishment of a devolved Northern Ireland Assembly, which has led to increased political and economic co-operation between the neighbouring countries.

If you are asked the above question with reference to a European region you should discuss cultural differences in Belgium as addressed in Topic 12 (Question 4).

Topic **21**
General Questions on Regional Geography

This section deals with general questions on regional geography where you are not specifically asked about physical processes or primary, secondary or tertiary activities. You will still use the information on the regions you have studied to answer, however the difficult part of these questions is recognising exactly what you are being asked.

LQ **1. Examine one economic challenge facing a European region you have studied.**

When the word **economic** is found in a question such as this it means your answer will come from primary, secondary or tertiary activities. The word **challenge** refers to a problem. The only types of regions you have studied which have economic problems are peripheral regions and you have only studied one peripheral region in Europe. Therefore the first two sentences of your answer to this question should be:

> The region I have studied is the Mezzogiorno. An economic challenge facing this region is the development of its primary [or secondary or tertiary] sector.

You would then go on to discuss that sector in detail.

LQ **2. Explain, with reference to an example you have studied, the development of one economic core region in Europe.**

Again this question contains the word **economic** so your answer will come from either one or a combination of primary, secondary or tertiary activities. You have only studied one core economic region in Europe so the opening lines of your answer to this question should be:

> The region I have studied is the Paris Basin. This region has developed as an economic core region as a result of its productive primary sector and well-developed secondary sector.

You would then discuss the primary sector for over half a page and then write an equal amount on the secondary sector. It is important to repeat the words of the question throughout your answer.

3. 'A region is an area which may be identified by one or more
LQ   characteristics.' Briefly explain this statement using a sketch map to
illustrate an example.

This question allows you to choose any one of your regions and talk about one or more characteristics of that region. When the word **characteristics** is in a question it means you can talk about physical, human or economic (primary, secondary and tertiary) characteristics. Remember, you have roughly fifteen minutes to complete a thirty-mark question in the Leaving Certificate. Therefore the opening lines for this question could be the following:

> The region I have studied is the West of Ireland. This region can be identified by its distinctive physical and economic characteristics.

You would then write about the physical characteristics of the region for about six minutes and the economic characteristics (primary, secondary and/or tertiary) for the same amount of time. Your answer must also include a sketch map illustrating the characteristics discussed.

Section **3**

Suggested Timings for the Exam

The total time available for the Leaving Certificate exam is two hours and fifty minutes (170 mins).

For **higher level**, time may be allocated as follows:

Section 1: Short questions	20 mins
Section 2: Physical geography	40 mins
Section 3: Regional geography	40 mins
Section 4: Human/economic geography	40 mins
Section 5: Optional section	30 mins

For **ordinary level**, time may be allocated as follows:

Section 1: Short questions	30 mins
Section 2: Physical geography	45 mins
Section 3: Regional geography	45 mins
Section 4: Elective geography	45 mins

This allows five minutes to read back over your answers at the end of the exam.